WHEN DID IGNORANCE BECOME A POINT OF VIEW?

Other DILBERT books from Boxtree

Dilbert-A Treasury of Sunday Strips: Version 00
ISBN: 0-7522-7232-2

Random Acts of Management
ISBN: 0-7522-7174-1

Dilbert Gives You the Business
ISBN: 0-7522-2394-1

Don't Step in the Leadership
ISBN: 0-7522-2389-5

Journey to Cubeville
ISBN: 0-7522-2384-4

I'm Not Anti-Business, I'm Anti-Idiot
ISBN: 0-7522-2379-8

Seven Years of Highly Defective People
ISBN: 0-7522-2407-7

Casual Day Has Gone Too Far
ISBN: 0-7522-1119-6

Fugitive from the Cubicle Police
ISBN: 0-7522-2431-X

Still Pumped from Using the Mouse
ISBN: 0-7522-2265-1

It's Obvious You Won't Survive by Your Wits Alone
ISBN: 0-7522-0201-4

Bring Me the Head of Willy the Mailboy!
ISBN: 0-7522-0136-0

Shave the Whales
ISBN: 0-7522-0849-7

Always Postpone Meetings with Time-Wasting Morons
ISBN: 0-7522-0854-3

Excuse Me While I Wag
ISBN: 0-7522-2399-2

WHEN DID IGNORANCE BECOME A POINT OF VIEW?

A DILBERT™ BOOK

BY SCOTT ADAMS

First published 2001 by Andrews McMeel Publishing, an Andrews McMeel Universal company,
4520 Main Street, Kansas City, Missouri 64111

First published in Great Britain 2001 by Boxtree
an imprint of Pan Macmillan Ltd
Pan Macmillan, 20 New Wharf Road, London N1 9RR
Basingstoke and Oxford
Associated companies throughout the world
www.panmacmillan.com

ISBN 0 7522 2412 3

www.dilbert.com

9 8 7 6 5 4 3 2 1

A CIP catalogue record for this book is available from the British Library

Printed by the Bath Press Ltd, Bath

For Tom-a-to and Tom-ah-to's mother

Introduction

Recently a woman called me and said she had no idea who I was but she had been told by someone — she couldn't remember who — that I give money to people like her. The woman said that she and her husband had nine kids and had moved to a desert in the Middle East. Now they were having difficulty supporting themselves because, well, they had nine kids and had moved to a desert. She figured the best solution was to call me and ask if I would support the entire family indefinitely. If you have nine children and think it's a good idea to move to the desert it is fair to say that you are not a good decision maker. So the question I had to ask myself was this: If I gave her money, would she be more likely to a) use it to feed and educate her children, or b) grunt out nine more children and move to a dislodged glacier floating in the Arctic Ocean?

The interesting part of the conversation came after I politely declined her invitation to fund the nonstop production of doomed babies. She got mad at me. Apparently she analyzed her situation and came to the conclusion that the root cause of her problem was the unwillingness of total strangers in other countries to give her money. And her solution to that problem was to get angry.

You might be wondering, as I was, whether this woman was actually a con artist who wasn't very good at her job, possibly an intern or a trainee. Maybe the experienced con artists in her office were playing a practical joke on her: "Tell him you're stupid and you need money to produce more people like you." I'll never know the real story. But it reminded me of all the times that my point of view differed from other people's.

For example, our current system of world government involves giving the leaders of all the major countries access to buttons that can launch missiles and vaporize unsuspecting citizens. I think a better system would be if every world leader had to walk around with a sack of explosives on his back and every citizen had access to a wristwatch button that would detonate it. My concept has many benefits beyond the obvious entertainment factor and the reduced risk of being vaporized by an incoming missile. For one thing, there would no longer be any such thing as a "slow news day." And the boring pack of lies called the State of the Union speech would last about thirty seconds. I have to think taxes would be abolished altogether. We wouldn't need all the tax money anyway: The military would be unnecessary and the economic stimulus from eliminating taxes would make all the poor people incredibly wealthy, or so I've been told. And if we needed a highway or a dam built, we could give our president a trowel and then place one finger menacingly over the wristwatch button and say, "Start working, Goober." I realize that my concept would degrade the prestige of the presidency, but I don't think that prestige was doing me any good anyway.

Speaking of world leaders, there's still time to join Dogbert's New Ruling Class (DNRC) and rule by his side when he conquers the planet and makes everyone else our domestic servants. To become a member of the DNRC, just sign up for the free Dilbert newsletter that is distributed whenever I feel like it, usually four times a year.

To subscribe or unsubscribe, go to www.dilbert.com. If you have problems with the automated subscription method, write to newsletter@unitedmedia.com.

S. Adams

Scott Adams

ASOK, THIS WILL BE THE MOST IMPORTANT ASSIGNMENT IN YOUR ENTIRE CAREER.
YOU MUST AFFIX THE ASSET TAGS IN THIS FOLDER TO OUR OFFICE EQUIPMENT.
BWAA-WAH-AH!!
HE MUST BE HAVING PROBLEMS AT HOME.
MY ASSIGNMENT IS TO PUT ASSET TAGS ON ALL EQUIPMENT.
DID YOU KNOW THAT STAPLERS ARE NOT CONSIDERED EQUIPMENT?
NO ONE LIKES TO MAKE CONVERSATION WITH THE ASSET TAG MAN.

AS CEO, I THANK YOU FOR MAKING ME OBSCENELY WEALTHY.
YESTERDAY I BUILT A GUEST HOUSE USING BUNDLES OF CASH AS BRICKS.

I NEED A NEW SPEECH WRITER.

I'VE BEEN ASKED TO SUMMARIZE MY PROJECT INTO THREE BULLET POINTS.
I HAD TO INVENT SOME NEW WORDS.
BELIEVE ME, YOU DON'T WANT TO BE ANY OF THESE THINGS.
· SPLURBY
· NOOBAH
· PIZKWAT
5/4/00 © 2000 United Feature Syndicate, Inc.
I'M STARTING TO GET AN INFERIORITY COMPLEX.
IF IT MAKES YOU FEEL BETTER, THAT ISN'T A COMPLEX.
NOW IF YOU'LL EXCUSE ME, I GOTTA TAKE A WICKED WAG.
5/5/00 © 2000 United Feature Syndicate, Inc.
I NEED TO TAKE A CLASS TO LEARN THE NEW TECH-NOLOGY.
TRADE RAG
OUR VENDOR'S SALES PERSON WILL TEACH YOU EVERYTHING HE KNOWS.
TRADE
YOU ONLY NEED THREE "MOIST TOWELETTES" TO GIVE YOURSELF A SPONGE BATH.
5/6/00 © 2000 United Feature Syndicate, Inc.

WHICH PRESIDENTIAL CANDIDATE DO YOU LIKE?
I STRONGLY FAVOR THE ONE WITH THE FUNNY HAIR. I FORGOT HIS NAME.
HIS SOCIAL POLICIES ARE THE EXACT OPPOSITE OF YOUR VIEWS.
REALLY?
WELL, I LIKE HIS TAX PLAN.
EVERY CREDIBLE ECONOMIST THINKS IT'S A BAD PLAN.
OH
©2000 United Feature Syndicate, Inc.
5/7/00
IT'S A GOOD THING WE TALKED BEFORE YOU POLLUTED THE SYSTEM WITH YOUR VOTE.
DO YOU WANT TO MAKE OUT?
SHE CLAIMED TO LIKE INTELLIGENT MEN, BUT SHE LIED.

I'VE DECIDED TO BECOME A GENERIC SELF-HELP CONSULTANT.
I'LL TELL PEOPLE TO KEEP A JOURNAL OF ALL THEIR THOUGHTS. THEN I'LL BILL THEM.
© 2000 United Feature Syndicate, Inc.
5/8/00
HOW WOULD THAT HELP ANYONE?
I LEAD BY EXAMPLE, MY FRIEND.

YOU CAN LOSE WEIGHT IF YOU WRITE DOWN ALL OF YOUR MEALS IN A JOURNAL.
THAT'S ALL I NEED TO DO?
YES, IF YOU USE OUR PATENTED WEIGHT-LOSS PENCIL.
© 2000 United Feature Syndicate, Inc.
5/9/00

THIS PRODUCT WOULD MELT THE POLAR ICE CAPS AND DOOM HUMANITY.
THAT'S OKAY.
YOU'RE PART OF HUMAN-ITY.
NO, I'M IN MARKET-ING.
© 2000 United Feature Syndicate, Inc.
5/10/00
I WON'T HELP YOU DESTROY THE PLANET.
THAT'S WHAT I SAID UNTIL I SAW THE FREE T-SHIRTS.

MY MARKETING PLAN CALLS FOR THE ANNIHILATION OF ALL LIFE ON EARTH.
OUR ONLY SERIOUS COMPETITOR IS A COMPANY THAT SELLS TOBACCO AND JUNK FOOD.
I'D LIKE VOLUN-TEERS.
I NEED SOME ACCOMPLISHMENTS FOR MY QUARTERLY REVIEW.
5/11/00 © 2000 United Feature Syndicate, Inc.

TO THE UNTRAINED EYE IT MIGHT LOOK AS IF I DO NO WORK.
BUT INSIDE HERE IS A RAGING SEA OF KNOWLEDGE MANAGEMENT AND STRATEGIC THINKING.
DID YOU HEAR THAT GURGLING SOUND?
5/12/00 © 2000 United Feature Syndicate, Inc.

DOGBERT CONSULTS
MY TEAM CAN BUILD AN E-COMMERCE SITE FOR YOU.
IT WILL BE SO WELL-DOCUMENTED THAT YOUR I.S. GROUP CAN EASILY MAINTAIN IT.
BUT THE COOLEST PART IS THAT THE DOCUMENTATION WILL BE DELIVERED BY FLYING PIGS!
5/13/00 © 2000 United Feature Syndicate, Inc.

CAROL, FROM NOW ON, I WANT A LIVE PERSON ANSWERING MY PHONE.
WHAT ATTRACTED YOU TO THAT IDEA?
WAS IT THE INEFFICIENCY OR THE DRAIN ON MORALE?
IMPORTANT EXECUTIVES DON'T USE VOICE MAIL.
I HAVE SOME INFORMATION FOR YOU.
CALL ME.
Beep Boop Beep Beep Boop Beep Beep
HE'S NOT HERE. DO YOU WANT TO LEAVE A DETAILED MESSAGE?
YES.
WELL, YOU CAN'T!!!
5/14/00
© 2000 United Feature Syndicate, Inc.

I SCHEDULED A MEETING WITH YOUR BOSS.
HE'LL PROBABLY ASK ME TO SPEAK FRANKLY ABOUT ANY PROBLEMS IN THE DEPARTMENT.
5/15/00 © 2000 United Feature Syndicate, Inc.
THIS COULDN'T GET ANY WORSE.
HE'S CUTE. I MIGHT ASK HIM OUT.

UM... HOW WAS YOUR MEETING WITH MY BOSS?
WE EACH TOLD OUR FAVORITE STORIES ABOUT YOU. THEN WE LAUGHED AND LAUGHED.
5/16/00 © 2000 United Feature Syndicate, Inc.
HE HAS STORIES ABOUT ME?
HE THOUGHT THEY WERE URBAN LEGENDS.

ALICE, MAYBE WE SHOULDN'T DATE. I'M A VP AND YOU'RE AN ENGINEER IN MY DIVISION.
SHEESH. GET OVER YOURSELF. I'M JUST USING YOU TO DRIVE MY BOSS NUTS.
5/17/00 © 2000 United Feature Syndicate, Inc.
YOUR INDIFFERENCE AROUSES ME! I WILL MAKE YOU MINE!
VPs

VP STALKS ALICE
I BROUGHT YOU A BOUQUET, ALICE.
THAT'S A BUNCH OF PENCILS, NOT A FLOWER BOUQUET.
REALLY?
MAY I USE YOUR PHONE? I NEED TO FIRE MY SECRETARY.
5/18/00 © 2000 United Feature Syndicate, Inc.

PERFORMANCE REVIEW
YOU DIDN'T SHOW ANY INITIATIVE THIS YEAR.
THAT'S YOUR FAULT FOR CREATING AN ATMOSPHERE OF FEAR AND DISTRUST.
YOU, YOU, YOU.
NOTE TO SELF: INCREASE FEAR.
5/19/00 © 2000 United Feature Syndicate, Inc.

PERFORMANCE REVIEW
DO YOU HAVE ANY WEAKNESSES THAT NEED IMPROVEMENT?
SOMETIMES I WORK SO FAST THAT I BECOME INVISIBLE.
IF I SEEM BLURRY RIGHT NOW, IT'S BECAUSE I'M MULTI-TASKING.
ONCE A YEAR IS WAY TOO OFTEN FOR THIS.
5/20/00 © 2000 United Feature Syndicate, Inc.

CAN YOU EXPLAIN WHY YOUR PROJECT IS BEHIND SCHEDULE?
YES. A SCHEDULE IS AN ARTIFICIAL DEVICE CREATED WITHOUT KNOWLEDGE OF THE FUTURE.
WILD GUESSES ARE USED AS SURROGATES FOR KNOWLEDGE.
PROJECT DEADLINES ARE TIED TO TRADE SHOW DATES INSTEAD OF REALITY.
THEN MANAGEMENT CUTS THE BUDGET UNTIL FAILURE IS ASSURED.
© 2000 United Feature Syndicate, Inc.
I ASSUME YOU CALLED ME HERE SO YOU CAN APOLOGIZE FOR YOUR ROLE IN ALL THIS.
WOULD YOU LIKE TO HEAR HOW BUDGETS ARE CREATED?

YOUR NEW CEO IS THE MOST POWERFUL WOMAN IN THE HI-TECH INDUSTRY.
I RECOMMEND EXPLOITING HER FAME IN YOUR ADVERTISEMENTS.
5/22/00 © 2000 United Feature Syndicate, Inc.
WHY DO I HAVE TO BE THE ONE TO SUGGEST IT?
CEOs LOVE THIS SORT OF THING.

MY CONSULTANT THINKS YOU SHOULD BE FEATURED IN OUR AD CAMPAIGN.
IS THAT BECAUSE I'M YOUR NEW CEO AND THE MOST POWERFUL WOMAN IN OUR INDUSTRY?
5/23/00 © 2000 United Feature Syndicate, Inc.
UM... YES, THAT'S WHY.
REMEMBER TO ASK ABOUT TAN LINES.

CEO AS SPOKESPERSON
SHOULDN'T I HOLD UP OUR PRODUCT INSTEAD OF LEAN-ING ON A CHAIR?

NO!
5/24/00 © 2000 United Feature Syndicate, Inc.

THAT HELPED YOUR HAIR BUT YOU'RE STILL DRESSED LIKE A NUN.

CEO AS SPOKESPERSON
WHAT DOES THIS POSE HAVE TO DO WITH OUR PRODUCT?
I'LL USE BLUE SCREEN TECHNOLOGY TO ADD IMPORTANT ELEMENTS LATER.
5/25/00 © 2000 United Feature Syndicate, Inc.
MY BLOUSE IS BLUE.
FIVE MINUTES.

AT TEN YOU'LL BE FIRING TED.
I'LL ORGANIZE HIS GOODBYE PARTY.
DO YOU KNOW WHAT WOULD BE MORE EFFICIENT?
5/26/00 © 2000 United Feature Syndicate, Inc.
WHAT HAPPENS AFTER WE YELL "SURPRISE"?

WE KNOW THESE RANDOM DRUG TESTS ARE UN-PLEASANT FOR EMPLOYEES.
5/27/00 © 2000 United Feature Syndicate, Inc.
THAT'S WHY WE OFFER FREE CASHEWS.
SUDDENLY I THOUGHT ABOUT CHARLIE BROWN BUT I DON'T KNOW WHY.

PSSST
YES?
COME IN AND SHUT THE DOOR.
I BOUGHT A FAKE VIDEO SURVEILLANCE CAMERA.
INSTALL IT IN THE BREAK ROOM TONIGHT.
IT'S CHEAPER THAN A REAL CAMERA AND IT WILL DISCOURAGE THEFTS.
© 2000 United Feature Syndicate, Inc.
5/28/00
IF YOU TREAT EMPLOYEES LIKE CRIMINALS, THEY'LL LEAVE.
GOOD POINT.
YOU'D BETTER HIDE THE FAKE CAMERA SO NO ONE KNOWS IT'S THERE.
TRASH

MY SOCKS USE AN ANTIMICROBIAL POLYMER TO BOND CHLORINE ATOMS TO COTTON.
I CAN WEAR THESE BABIES FOR DAYS BEFORE THEY START TO STINK.
WHAT WAS THAT OTHER PICK-UP LINE WE TALKED ABOUT?
IT WAS "HI."
© 2000 United Feature Syndicate, Inc.
5/29/00
MY PATENT FOR NO-CLICK SHOPPING WAS GRANTED.
I'M SURE SOME WHINERS WILL SAY IT'S AN OBVIOUS IDEA.
YOU'D BETTER CLICK SOMETHING OR I HAVE TO SHIP YOU SOME BOOKS.
© 2000 United Feature Syndicate, Inc.
5/30/00

I'M DOCUMENTING EVERYTHING YOU DO SO I CAN EASILY FIRE YOU SOMEDAY.
MAYBE YOU COULD CALL ME IF YOU DO ANYTHING.
LEAVE IT HERE AND I'LL FILL IT OUT FOR YOU.
© 2000 United Feature Syndicate, Inc.
5/31/00

THE FIVE HUNDRED DOLLAR MORALE IMPROVEMENT AWARD GOES TO ED.
GAA!! IT'S ONLY $240 AFTER TAXES!!!
6/1/00 © 2000 United Feature Syndicate, Inc.
SO THAT'S WHAT GOOD MORALE LOOKS LIKE.
APPARENTLY WE'VE HAD IT THE WHOLE TIME.

MING, EVERYONE SAYS OUR WEB SITE IS UGLY.
REALLY? EVERY PERSON ON EARTH SAID THAT?
EVEN TIBETAN MONKS?
6/2/00 © 2000 United Feature Syndicate, Inc.
MAYBE IT WAS JUST ONE PERSON.
AND YOU CONFUSED HIM WITH THE ENTIRE PLANET?

IF I COULD TURN INVISIBLE, I WOULDN'T NEED TO MAKE DECISIONS.

INVISIBLE... INVISIBLE... YOU CAN'T SEE ME.
6/3/00 © 2000 United Feature Syndicate, Inc.
I GUESS WE'RE DONE.
RUN SILENT.

CATBERT: EVIL H.R. DIRECTOR
WALLY, OUR AUDITORS FOUND 40 GIGABITS OF BIKINI PICTURES ON YOUR PC.
THAT IS GROUNDS FOR DISMISSAL. HOW DO YOU PLEAD?
INNOCENT.
TECHNICALLY, THEY DIDN'T FIND ANY PICTURES.
WHAT THEY FOUND WERE ZEROES AND ONES RESTING HARMLESSLY ON MAGNETIC MEDIA.
IT WAS THE AUDITORS THEMSELVES WHO ACTIVATED THOSE HARMLESS BITS TO FORM PICTURES ON THE SCREEN!
I DEMAND THAT THOSE GODLESS AUDITORS BE FIRED!
AND IF IT'S NOT TOO MUCH TROUBLE, I'D LIKE MY ZEROES AND ONES BACK.
WAS JUSTICE SERVED?
IT'S A GRAY AREA.
6/4/00 ©2000 United Feature Syndicate, Inc.

I AM MORDAC, THE PREVENTER OF INFORMATION SERVICES!
I AM WEB MISTRESS MING!
YOUR FIREWALL IS INADEQUATE. YOU MUST BE PUNISHED!
YOUR HTML IS WEAK! YOU MUST BE PUNISHED.
6/5/00 © 2000 United Feature Syndicate, Inc.
I MUST HAVE YOU!
TALK COBOL TO ME, BABY.

MING, I'M MOVING YOUR WEB MISTRESS FUNCTION TO I.S. YOU'LL REPORT TO MORDAC.
NO-O-O-O-O-O
6/6/00 © 2000 United Feature Syndicate, Inc.
WE CAN STILL DATE BUT I FEEL OBLIGED TO HATE YOUR GUTS NOW.
IT WORKS FOR ME.

DEAREST MING,
MY LOVE FOR YOU IS BOUNDLESS.
MORDAC

P.S. IF YOU DON'T STOP PUTTING FOOD GARBAGE IN THE RECYCLING BIN YOU WILL BE TERMINATED.
6/7/00 © 2000 United Feature Syndicate, Inc.

NEVER DATE YOUR BOSS.
OKAY.

HI, I'M EDFRED, THE TWO-FACED EMPLOYEE.
IF YOU TELL YOUR BOSS HIS NEW PLAN IS STUPID I'LL BACK YOU UP.
REALLY?
I DON'T LIKE THE LOOKS OF THIS.
© 2000 United Feature Syndicate, Inc.
6/8/00

I DISAGREE WITH DILBERT. THE BOSS'S PLAN IS BRILLIANT.
YOUR OTHER FACE AGREED WITH ME TWO MINUTES AGO!
WHAT OTHER FACE?
NO. . . I STILL JUST SEE THE ONE.
© 2000 United Feature Syndicate, Inc.
6/9/00

I'VE DECIDED TO MANAGE LIKE A SADISTIC GAME SHOW HOST.
BECAUSE IT WOULD BE INSANE IF I KEPT DOING WHAT DIDN'T WORK.
WOULD YOU RATHER HAVE A PERFORMANCE REVIEW OR BE PECKED TO DEATH BY TRAINED BIRDS?
© 2000 United Feature Syndicate, Inc.
6/10/00

I CUT YOUR BUDGET IN HALF.
HOW CAN I DO A TECHNOLOGY INSTALLATION WITHOUT AN ADEQUATE BUDGET?!
TRY BEING UNETHICAL WITH OUR VENDORS.
WHAT?
IT'S EASY.
TELL THEM WE MIGHT MAKE A HUGE PURCHASE LATER...
...IF THEY GIVE US A BUNCH OF FREE STUFF NOW.
6/11/00 ©2000 United Feature Syndicate, Inc.
IF IT MAKES YOU FEEL BETTER, WAIT UNTIL THEY LIE FIRST.
AND THERE ARE NO HIDDEN COSTS.
UM...WE MIGHT MAKE A HUGE PURCHASE LATER.

DOGBERT CONSULTS
ALL OF YOUR EMPLOYEES ARE IGNORANT.
I CAN FIX THAT BY SELLING YOU INTRANET COLLABORATION TOOLS.
BUT IF THEY'RE SHARING THEIR IGNORANCE...
SIGN IT SIGN IT SIGN IT
6/12/00 © 2000 United Feature Syndicate, Inc.

WHO WANTS TO SHARE KNOWLEDGE WITH ME VIA OUR NEW INTRA-NET COLLABORATION SOFTWARE?
YOU DON'T HAVE ANY KNOWLEDGE TO SHARE.
OUCH.
IT HURTS BECAUSE IT'S TRUE.
I'M HOARDING MY KNOWLEDGE IN CASE I EVER NEED IT.
6/13/00 © 2000 United Feature Syndicate, Inc.

DOGBERT CONSULTS
NO ONE USES THE INTRANET COLLAB-ORATION SOFTWARE YOU SOLD US.
YOUR EMPLOYEES ARE DEFECTIVE. I RECOMMEND CAT SCANS.
THIS ONE IS DEFECTIVE TOO.
NEXT IN LINE!
6/14/00 © 2000 United Feature Syndicate, Inc.

MY ACCOMPLISHMENT THIS WEEK WAS SCHEDULING FIFTY PEOPLE TO DISCUSS THE BUG IN OUR PRODUCT.

I FIXED THE BUG THIS MORNING.
6/15/00 © 2000 United Feature Syndicate, Inc.

AND THANKS FOR NOT INVITING ME TO THE MEETING.

OUR SERVER NAMED "POINTY" IS OVER-LOADED.
SO WE'RE MOVING SOME OF THE LOAD TO "HAIRED" AND "IDIOT."
BUT WE STILL NEED A NEW SERVER.
6/16/00 © 2000 United Feature Syndicate, Inc.
HE SIGNED THE PURCHASE ORDER FOR "CLUELESS".

UH-OH...SUDDENLY THIS MEETING AND ALL THE STRANGE WORDS MAKE SENSE.
POW!!
6/17/00 © 2000 United Feature Syndicate, Inc.
IT'S YOUR TURN TO BUY THE CARD.

WELCOME TO WORK-PLACE VIOLENCE PREVENTION TRAINING.
HOW CAN WE IDENTIFY POTENTIALLY VIOLENT EMPLOYEES?
OOH! OOH!
WALLY?
DO THEY HAVE BEARDS?
© 2000 United Feature Syndicate, Inc.
6/18/00
UM...NO
THAT WAS A STUPID ANSWER.
VIOLENT EMPLOYEES ARE USUALLY CREEPY, INEFFECTIVE MALES WHO ARE WIDELY DISRESPECTED.
MAY I CHANGE SEATS?

MING, OUR WEB SITE NEEDS A FAQ SECTION.
I FIND YOUR SUGGESTION IGNORANT AND WITHOUT MERIT.
AWAY WITH YOU.
6/19/00 © 2000 United Feature Syndicate, Inc.
SO...ARE YOU DOING ANYTHING THIS WEEKEND?
GAAA!!

HELP ME UNDER-STAND THE MALE BRAIN, DILBERT.
I TREAT YOU LIKE DIRT AND YOU ASK ME OUT ON A DATE?
6/20/00 © 2000 United Feature Syndicate, Inc.
GOOD PERSONALITIES ARE OVERRATED.
YOU'RE GETTING ME ALL HOT OVER HERE.

FRANKLY, I'M INSULTED THAT YOU ASKED ME OUT.
IT MEANS YOU THINK WE'RE ABOUT THE SAME LEVEL OF ATTRAC-TIVENESS.
6/21/00 © 2000 United Feature Syndicate, Inc.

YOU'D BETTER HAVE ONE HECKUVA SEXY CAR.
IT'S ELECTRIC.

I DON'T LIKE TO TALK ON DATES. DO YOU MIND IF I HUM?

THAT'S OKAY. I'LL PRETEND YOU'RE THE RADIO.
6/22/00 © 2000 United Feature Syndicate, Inc.
HMM MM-MM MM-M-M MMMM
I NEED A NEW RADIO.

DO YOU MIND IF I CHATTER NONSTOP ABOUT PEOPLE YOU DON'T KNOW?
NO.
DO YOU MIND IF I GAWK AT EVERY WOMAN WHO WALKS BY?
YES.
6/23/00 © 2000 United Feature Syndicate, Inc.
IN FACT, I WOULD APPRECIATE IT IF YOU DISPLAYED NO MALE TRAITS WHATSOEVER.
CAN DO.

YEAH, I'M HAVING THE WORST DATE EVER.
I'LL CHECK.
WHAT'S THAT ON THE GROUND? IT LOOKS INTERESTING.
6/24/00 © 2000 United Feature Syndicate, Inc.
NOT SO GOOD.

I'M GROSSLY UNDERPAID.
I WANT A RAISE.
OH, DILBERT, DILBERT, DILBERT.
WHAT?
WHAT?
WHAT?
PEOPLE DON'T WORK HERE FOR THE MONEY.
THEY WORK HERE FOR THE CHALLENGE!
6/25/00 © 2000 United Feature Syndicate, Inc.
IF CHALLENGES ARE MORE VALUABLE THAN MONEY...
WHY DON'T YOU GIVE ME YOUR MONEY AND I'LL GIVE YOU MY CHALLENGES?
WELL?
I MUST KILL HIM BEFORE HE INFECTS THE OTHERS.

. . . AND THAT'S THE PLAN.
YIPPEE!
WOO-HA!!
I'M VERY INSPIRING LATELY.
HOW DID PEOPLE SURVIVE MEETINGS BEFORE THESE THINGS?
WEBVAN SPLIT!
© 2000 United Feature Syndicate, Inc.
6/26/00

YOU'VE GOT TO WORK EIGHTEEN HOURS A DAY TO COMPETE IN THIS INDUSTRY!
LET'S JUST SAY WE WORK EIGHTEEN HOURS A DAY. MAYBE OUR COMPETITORS WILL DIE TRYING TO MATCH US.
WOULD THAT WORK?
IT ALMOST WORKED ON US.
© 2000 United Feature Syndicate, Inc.
6/27/00

RATBERT IS OUR NEW COMPANY CONCIERGE.
I WILL PERFORM ANY ERRAND, NO MATTER HOW PERSONAL OR DEGRADING IT IS.
I NEED A LOOFAH.
LATHER ME UP!
© 2000 United Feature Syndicate, Inc.
6/28/00

RATBERT THE CONCIERGE
I'D LIKE A DATE WITH A WOMAN WHO THINKS I'M HOT.
REMEMBER, YOU PROMISED YOU WOULD DO ANY ERRAND FOR EMPLOYEES.
© 2000 United Feature Syndicate, Inc. 6/29/00
TELL ME AGAIN HOW HOT I AM.
COMPANY CONCIERGE
I DON'T HAVE TIME FOR MY DOCTOR APPOINTMENT.
GO IN MY PLACE AND TELL HIM YOU'RE HAVING TROUBLE SLEEPING AT YOUR DESK.
© 2000 United Feature Syndicate, Inc. 6/30/00
AND DON'T LET HIM SWEET-TALK YOU ABOUT DIET AND EXERCISE. I WANT PILLS!
COMPANY CONCIERGE
I NEED AN ALIBI.
THE POLICE WILL TRY TO BEAT THE TRUTH OUT OF YOU, BUT DON'T LET THEM BREAK YOU!
© 2000 United Feature Syndicate, Inc. 7/1/00
I ALSO NEED LYE... AND A BARREL...
BETTER YET, MAKE THAT TWO BARRELS.

WE HAD FIFTEEN SYSTEM FAILURES WITH THE PREVIOUS SOFTWARE.
15
YOUR DATA AREN'T ACTIONABLE.
WHAT?
YOUR PRESENTATION HAS NO PRACTICAL VALUE.
WELL, IF THAT'S SUDDENLY A CRIME THEN CALL ME GUILTY!
NOW THE MEETING FEELS AWKWARD. CAN WE GO BACK TO ACTING INTERESTED?
I GUESS.
FINE. LET'S PUT THIS UGLY INCIDENT BEHIND US.
AND IF YOU MULTIPLY THE DIGITS YOU GET FIVE.
15
©2000 United Feature Syndicate, Inc.
7/2/00

DILBERT, YOU'LL BE WORKING WITH LULU. SHE'S ALMOST NORMAL.
BUT SHE HAS NO SENSE OF PROPORTION FOR PROBLEMS.
DID YOU NOTICE THAT HE LOOKED AT YOU FUNNY?
WHAT?!
© 2000 United Feature Syndicate, Inc.
7/3/00

THE ADVENTURES OF LULU
THE WOMAN WHO HAS NO SENSE OF PROPORTION
GAAA! DOES THIS MEAN YOU HATE ME?!!
IT'S CALLED AN ASSIGNMENT.
THIS IS WAR!
© 2000 United Feature Syndicate, Inc.
7/4/00

COME HELP ME ON THIS ASSIGNMENT. IT'S A HUGE CRISIS!
LULU, DO YOU EVER WONDER WHY YOUR LIFE IS A SERIES OF CRISES?
I ASSUME GOD IS SOFTENING ME UP BEFORE SMITING ME.
EXCUSE ME WHILE I PUT ON MY STATIC GUARD.
© 2000 United Feature Syndicate, Inc.
7/5/00

MY PROJECT WAS IN A DEATH SPIRAL.
I LEAPT INTO ACTION AND REORGANIZED MY FILING SYSTEM.
DID THAT HELP?
MY STRESS IS GONE!
7/6/00 © 2000 United Feature Syndicate, Inc.

THE EMPLOYEE OF THE MONTH IS LULU.
LULU OVERCAME LONG ODDS TO WIN THIS AWARD.
I.E., HER NAME WAS RANDOMLY PICKED.
I'D PROTEST BUT I DON'T WANT TO TAINT MY VICTORY OF LAST MONTH.
7/7/00 © 2000 United Feature Syndicate, Inc.

LULU, YOU'VE STALLED MY PROJECT FOR LONG ENOUGH. I WANT YOUR INPUT...

NOW!!

I FOUND OUT MY JAW UNHINGES WHEN I'M MAD.
YOU FRIGHTEN MY HOAGIE.
7/8/00 © 2000 United Feature Syndicate, Inc.

MY SOFTWARE WILL CREATE HUMAN SIMULATIONS FROM DNA SAMPLES.
WHAT'S THE MARKET APPLICATION?
WELL...THERE ARE MANY VARIOUS APPLICATIONS.
NAME ONE.
WELL...SOMEDAY THE ENTIRE HUMAN GENOME WILL BE MAPPED AND DECODED.
YOU COULD TAKE A HAIR SAMPLE FROM A WOMAN WHO REFUSES TO DATE YOU...
AND CREATE A SOFT-WARE SIMULATION OF HER TO KEEP IN YOUR COMPUTER WATCH.
YOU COULD HAVE ONE BUTTON TO FEED HER AND ONE BUTTON TO PUNISH HER.
I'D BUY IT.
CAN YOU ADD A BUTTON?
7/9/00

WRITE A PERFORMANCE EVALUATION FOR YOURSELF.
SHOOT FOR ABOUT A 3% RAISE...
BECAUSE THAT'S WHAT YOU'RE GETTING.
DILBERT'S INVENTIONS WILL EARN A BILLION DOLLARS. BUT WE THINK HE STEALS ALMOST AS MUCH.
7/10/00 © 2000 United Feature Syndicate, Inc.
DOGBERT CONSULTS
HERE'S A FREE SAMPLE OF MY WORK.
SO COMPANY "A" WAS MANAGED BY IDIOTS WITH NO WEB STRATEGY.
WHAT WOULD YOU RECOMMEND FOR MY COMPANY?
FIRST, CHANGE ITS NAME TO "A".
7/11/00 © 2000 United Feature Syndicate, Inc.

DOGBERT CONSULTS
I SAVED SOME MONEY BY BUYING A USED CONSULTING REPORT.
WE'RE GOING TO GIVE THE EXCLUSIVE RIGHTS FOR SOMETHING CALLED DOS TO SOMETHING CALLED MICROSOFT.
I HAVE A GOOD FEELING ABOUT THIS.
7/12/00 © 2000 United Feature Syndicate, Inc.

DOGBERT CONSULTS
I GOLF WITH YOUR CEO.
FOR A MILLION DOLLARS I CAN ACCIDENTALLY BEAN HIM WITH A GOLF BALL.
© 2000 United Feature Syndicate, Inc.
7/13/00
HE ALWAYS WEARS A HELMET.
NOT IN THE CLUBHOUSE.
THIS WEEK I WAS RENDERED USELESS BY THE STRESS OF BAD MANAGEMENT.
UM...
THAT'S SOMETHING WE ONLY SAY IN THE CAFETERIA.
© 2000 United Feature Syndicate, Inc.
7/14/00
YOU'RE DOING A TERRIFIC JOB!
TRY TO FIND A MIDDLE RANGE.

I GOT THE STRESS EVERYONE TALKS ABOUT. WHAT SHOULD I DO?
TRY USING IT AS AN EXCUSE FOR NOT EXERCISING.
© 2000 United Feature Syndicate, Inc.
7/15/00
SO... IT'S A GOOD THING?
IT MADE ME THE MAN I AM TODAY.

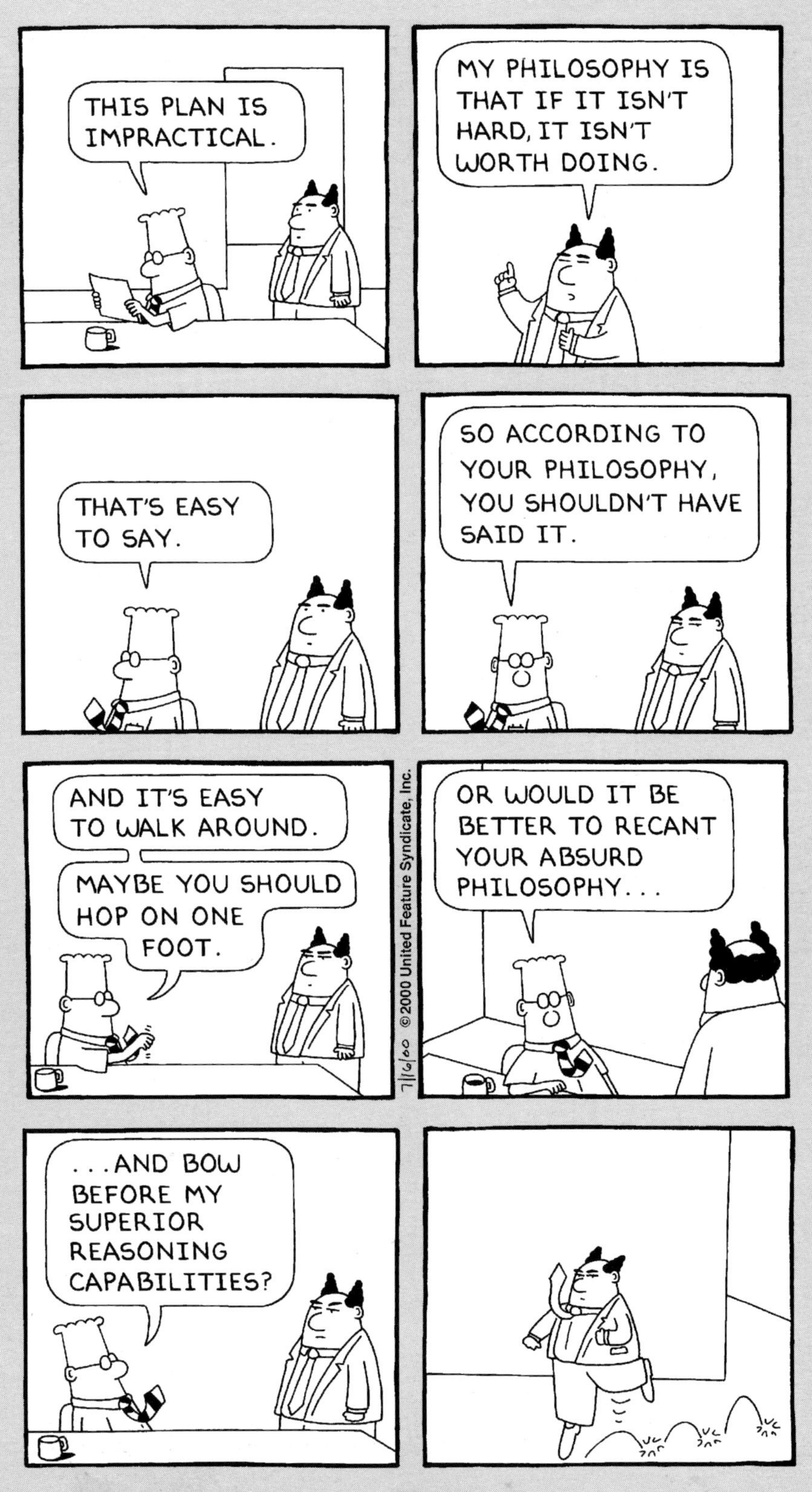
THIS PLAN IS IMPRACTICAL.
MY PHILOSOPHY IS THAT IF IT ISN'T HARD, IT ISN'T WORTH DOING.
THAT'S EASY TO SAY.
SO ACCORDING TO YOUR PHILOSOPHY, YOU SHOULDN'T HAVE SAID IT.
AND IT'S EASY TO WALK AROUND.
MAYBE YOU SHOULD HOP ON ONE FOOT.
OR WOULD IT BE BETTER TO RECANT YOUR ABSURD PHILOSOPHY...
...AND BOW BEFORE MY SUPERIOR REASONING CAPABILITIES?
7/16/00 ©2000 United Feature Syndicate, Inc.

I HEARD THAT YOU WON'T GIVE MARKETING THE INFORMATION THEY NEED.
I RESPECTFULLY DECLINE THE INVITATION TO JOIN YOUR HALLUCINATION.
© 2000 United Feature Syndicate, Inc.
YOUR SYSTEM WORKS.
NEXT TIME TRY SHORTENING IT TO "BAH".

THIS SPECIAL T-SHIRT IS AWARDED TO TED FOR ALL OF HIS ACHIEVEMENTS.
NEXT ON THE AGENDA...
© 2000 United Feature Syndicate, Inc.
WE'RE PLANNING SOME STAFF CUTS.

WE'LL BE SHUTTING DOWN OUR GLOBAL COMMUNICATIONS BUSINESS AND DE-ORBITING OUR SATELLITES.

QUESTION: WOULDN'T THAT CREATE DOZENS OF DEADLY FLAME BALLS SPEEDING TOWARD EARTH?
© 2000 United Feature Syndicate, Inc.
THAT'S WHY WE'RE AIMING FOR CITIES THAT HAVE LOTS OF SWIMMING POOLS.

OUR INVESTIGATIVE REPORTER HAS IDENTIFIED THE COMPANY BEHIND THE DEADLY FALLING SATELLITES.
WHUMP!
YOUR PLAN WORKED.
WHAT PLAN?
© 2000 United Feature Syndicate, Inc. 7/20/00
I'M TIRED OF GETTING NO RESPECT AT WORK.
NEW
I'M GOING TO SEND MY RÉSUMÉ TO A COMPANY THAT'S LOCATED IN A PLACE I'D NEVER WANT TO LIVE.
I WONDER WHY THEY DON'T RESPECT YOU.
THAT'S WHAT I WANT TO KNOW!
NEW
© 2000 United Feature Syndicate, Inc. 7/21/00
THERE...MY RÉSUMÉ IS DONE. I WILL NO LONGER BE A SLAVE TO MY COMPANY.
YEAH! NOW YOU'RE A POTENTIAL SLAVE FOR A COMPANY IN AN UNDESIRABLE LOCATION!
WAS THAT SARCASM OR SUPPORTIVENESS?
YOU ONLY THINK THERE'S A DIFFERENCE.
© 2000 United Feature Syndicate, Inc. 7/22/00

HAVE YOU MET THE NEW CIO?
NO.
I HEAR HE'S YOUNG.
HELLO.
WE NEED TO INTEGRATE OUR ENTERPRISE RESOURCE PLANNING WITH OUR EXISTING E-COMMERCE PLATFORM.
NOW IF YOU'LL EXCUSE ME, NATURE CALLS.
AAAHHH...
THEN WE'LL DE-CENTRALIZE THE PROCUREMENT FUNCTION AND...
HOLD ON A SECOND.
GRAMPS, COULD YOU DO ME A HUGE FAVOR?
7/23/00 ©2000 United Feature Syndicate, Inc.

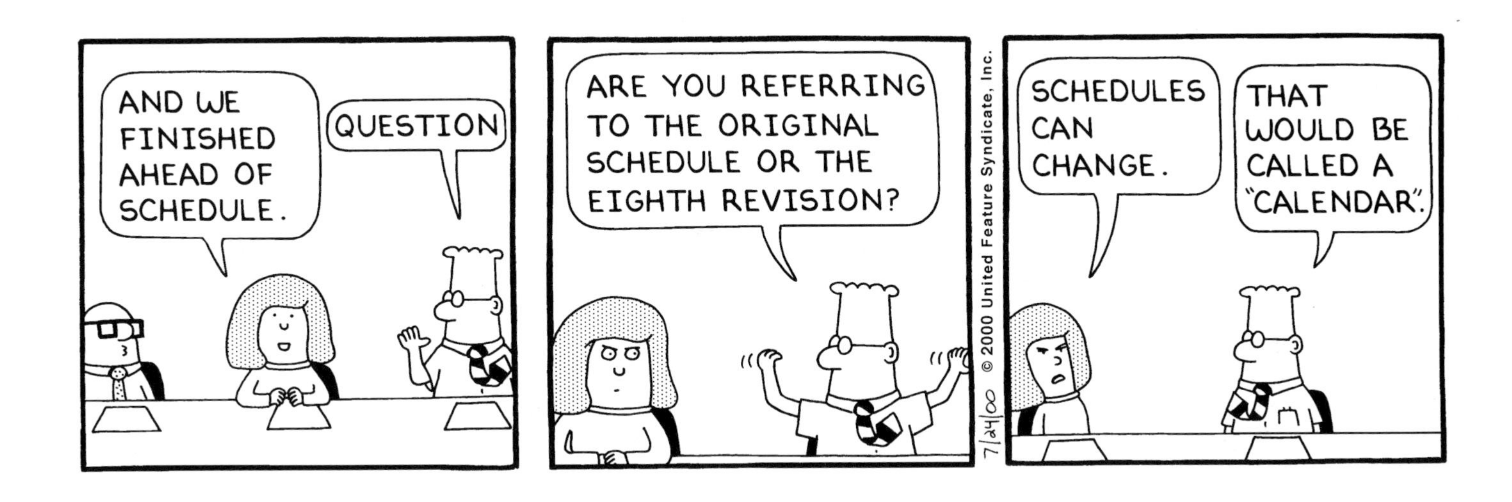
AND WE FINISHED AHEAD OF SCHEDULE.
QUESTION
ARE YOU REFERRING TO THE ORIGINAL SCHEDULE OR THE EIGHTH REVISION?
© 2000 United Feature Syndicate, Inc.
7/24/00
SCHEDULES CAN CHANGE.
THAT WOULD BE CALLED A "CALENDAR".

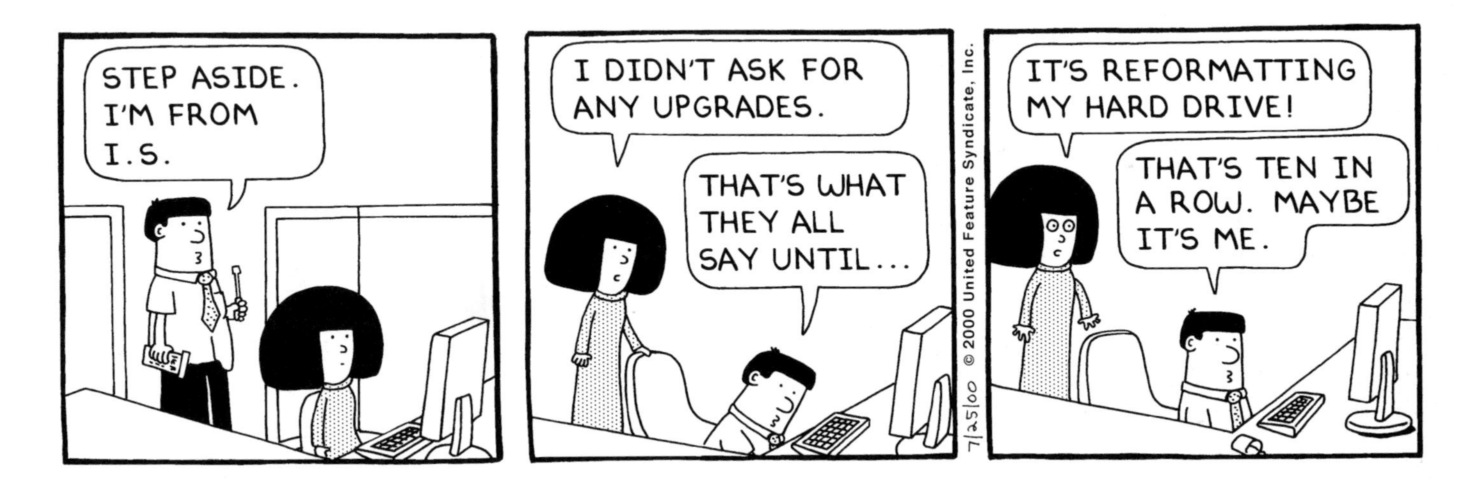
STEP ASIDE. I'M FROM I.S.
I DIDN'T ASK FOR ANY UPGRADES.
THAT'S WHAT THEY ALL SAY UNTIL...
© 2000 United Feature Syndicate, Inc.
7/25/00
IT'S REFORMATTING MY HARD DRIVE!
THAT'S TEN IN A ROW. MAYBE IT'S ME.

HOW LONG HAS HE BEEN UNDER YOUR DESK?
THREE DAYS.

DID YOU FEED HIM?
JUST SOME LICORICE.
© 2000 United Feature Syndicate, Inc.
7/26/00

YOU SHOULD NEVER FEED THE I.S. PEOPLE.
MORE LICORICE!

WELL, I UPGRADED THREE THINGS AND I ACCIDENTALLY BROKE THREE THINGS.
IN I.S. TERMS, I CAME OUT AHEAD.
DOES MY COMPUTER WORK?
NO, BUT IF IT DID, IT WOULD BE MUCH FASTER.
SNAP
7/27/00 © 2000 United Feature Syndicate, Inc.

I FINISHED UPGRADING THE SALES SUPPORT NETWORK.
IS THAT WHY I CAN'T UNLOCK MY LEXUS?!!
YOU DON'T OWN A LEXUS. YOU ONLY LOOK LIKE A GUY DOWN THE HALL WHO OWNS ONE.
I HATE THAT GUY.
7/28/00 © 2000 United Feature Syndicate, Inc.

THANKS TO YOU, MY COMPUTER SCREEN IS ALL FUZZY NOW!
?
YOU'RE ALWAYS FIDDLING WITH SOMETHING THAT MAKES SOMETHING ELSE STOP WORKING.
DON'T CLEAN YOUR SCREEN WITH YOUR HANDKERCHIEF DURING FLU SEASON.
STOP CHANGING THE SUBJECT.
7/29/00 © 2000 United Feature Syndicate, Inc.

HELP ME INTERVIEW A CANDIDATE FOR ENGINEERING.
UH-OH
I THINK HE'S TERRIFIC!
ACCORDING TO YOUR RESUMÉ, PAUL, YOU INVENTED E-COMMERCE.
WOW!
I'M GOING TO HIRE HIM RIGHT NOW!
HOLD ON.
PAUL, YOU DIDN'T REALLY INVENT E-COMMERCE, DID YOU?
WELL...
7/30/00 © 2000 United Feature Syndicate, Inc.
MAYBE I WAS... UM... PART OF THE TEAM THAT INVENTED IT.
NO ONE INVENTED E-COMMERCE!
WHEN CAN YOU START?
WHY AM I HERE?
MAYBE PAUL CAN TEACH YOU HOW TO INVENT THINGS.

CATBERT: EVIL H.R. DIRECTOR
YOU NEED MY APPROVAL FOR ANY OUTSIDE JOBS.
OH, MY...I HAVE THE SUDDEN REALIZATION THAT YOU CONTROL MY ENTIRE LIFE.
BUT YOU CAN'T CONTROL WHAT I THINK!
Employee will say, "You can't control what I Think!"
© 2000 United Feature Syndicate, Inc.
7/31/00

I PLAN TO SPEND THE NEXT YEAR ADDING AUTOMATIC REGISTRATION TO OUR PRODUCT.
IT ALREADY HAS THAT FEATURE.
OH.
© 2000 United Feature Syndicate, Inc.
8/1/00

TED, I'M GIVING YOU A PROMOTION IN TITLE.
WOW!
NOW YOU'RE THE SENIOR VICE DUKE AND IMPERIAL MAJESTY OF ALL ENGINEERING.
CAN I HAVE BUSINESS CARDS NOW?
NO, YOU'RE ONLY A VICE DUKE.
© 2000 United Feature Syndicate, Inc.
8/2/00

WE'RE GOING TO START TRACKING OUR TIME SPENT WITH INTERNAL CLIENTS.
I WILL CLEVERLY SEND FAKE BILLS TO OTHER DEPART-MENTS TO SHOW HOW HELPFUL WE ARE.
© 2000 United Feature Syndicate, Inc.
8/3/00
I CAN'T HELP YOU. I'M BUSY WITH MY TIME SHEET.

SOMEONE STOLE MY PURSE.
SO I USED MY NAVY SEAL TRAINING TO BOOBY-TRAP MY CUBICLE.
© 2000 United Feature Syndicate, Inc.
8/4/00
AAIEE!!!
THE MAIL IS EARLY TODAY.

ALICE, DID YOU BOOBY-TRAP YOUR CUBICLE?

THE QUESTION IS, WHY ARE YOU IN MY CUBICLE?
© 2000 United Feature Syndicate, Inc.
8/5/00

WHAT IF I PROMISE TO NEVER AGAIN BORROW YOUR GUEST CHAIR?

CATBERT: EVIL H.R. DIRECTOR
VIDEO CAMERAS HAVE BEEN INSTALLED IN ALL WORK AREAS.
EMPLOYEES MUST WEAR I.D. BADGES AROUND THEIR NECKS.
YOUR INTERNET AND TELEPHONE USAGE WILL BE MONITORED.
EVERYONE WILL UNDERGO MAN-DATORY DRUG TESTING.
THEY'RE NOT RESISTING.
THEY'RE READY FOR PHASE TWO.
PREPARE TO BE PERMANENTLY MARKED BY HOT IRONS.
WILL THAT HURT?
I'LL BE FINE. THANKS FOR ASKING.
WALLY IS ABOUT TO EXPERIENCE BRAND AWARENESS.
© 2000 United Feature Syndicate, Inc.
8/6/00

I WORK HARDER THAN YOU. WHY DO I GET PAID A FIFTH OF WHAT YOU MAKE?
THAT'S BECAUSE THERE ARE MANY PEOPLE LIKE YOU BUT FEW PEOPLE LIKE ME.
8/7/00 © 2000 United Feature Syndicate, Inc.
MAYBE THAT'S BECAUSE THE PEOPLE LIKE ME EVENTUALLY KILL THE PEOPLE LIKE YOU.
I SHOULD CREATE MY OWN LITTLE INTERNET START-UP.
ALL I NEED IS A BUSINESS PLAN.
8/8/00 © 2000 United Feature Syndicate, Inc.
THE V.C. ARE SICK OF B TO B.
THE VIET CONG ARE SICK OF BREAKFAST IN BED?

I'M NOT ALLOWED TO POACH EMPLOYEES IF I LEAVE THIS COMPANY.
BUT THERE'S NO LAW AGAINST YOU ASKING ME FOR A JOB...WINK WINK.
8/9/00 © 2000 United Feature Syndicate, Inc.
I'M NOT GOING TO WINK ALL DAY, YOU MORON!

HAVE YOU FINISHED MY BILLION DOLLAR BUSINESS PLAN YET?
ALMOST.
I'M UP TO THE PART WHERE THE S.E.C. INVESTIGATES YOU FOR SECURITIES FRAUD.
© 2000 United Feature Syndicate, Inc.
8/10/00
I CAN'T DECIDE WHAT THE EMPLOYEES WILL BE SINGING WHEN YOU GET HANDCUFFED.
I HAD PLANNED TO HIRE ANOTHER ENGINEER.
AT THE LAST MINUTE I REMEMBERED I COULD JUST MAKE YOU WORK TWICE AS HARD.
© 2000 United Feature Syndicate, Inc.
8/11/00
MAYBE YOU COULD NOMINATE ME FOR ONE OF THOSE COST-SAVING AWARDS.

TED, YOUR TEN YEAR SERVICE PARTY WILL BE ON TUESDAY.

I'M HAVING SURGERY TUESDAY.
© 2000 United Feature Syndicate, Inc.
8/12/00
MAYBE YOU COULD DROP OFF A CASSEROLE ON YOUR WAY.

THIS IS RASPUTIN, OUR NEW CONSULTANT.
HE STOPPED MY PAPER CUT FROM BLEEDING.
HE HAS CHARISMA.
I'D LIKE TO SEE A DEMONSTRATION ON ASOK.
ACK... CAN'T... BREATHE...
THAT'S CALLED THE EVIL EYE PROCESS.
NOW DO WALLY.
ACK... CAN'T... BREATHE...
HE NEVER HAD A CHANCE.
YOUR ANTI-CHARISMA IS STRONG TODAY.
8/13/00 ©2000 United Feature Syndicate, Inc.

I WAS SO MOTIVATED BY YOUR PEP TALK YESTERDAY THAT I CAME TO WORK TEN MINUTES EARLY!
WALLY, WE START AT EIGHT, NOT AT NINE.
© 2000 United Feature Syndicate, Inc.
8/14/00
THAT'S GONNA COST YOU TEN MINUTES.

OUR DISASTER RECOVERY PLAN GOES SOMETHING LIKE THIS...
HELP! HELP!
© 2000 United Feature Syndicate, Inc.
8/15/00
SOMEDAY WE HOPE TO HAVE A BUDGET.

AS YOU CAN CLEARLY SEE IN SLIDE 397...

GAAAAH!
Z
Z
© 2000 United Feature Syndicate, Inc.
8/16/00
"POWERPOINT" POISONING.

YOUR SALARY IS 115% OF THE MID-POINT FOR YOUR RANGE. ISN'T THAT EXCITING?
WHY DON'T YOU SAY IT'S 115% BELOW THE TOP OF THE RANGE WHICH CAN NEVER BE ACHIEVED UNDER OUR SYSTEM?
8/17/00
© 2000 United Feature Syndicate, Inc.
NO PEEKING AT THE SUPER-VISOR'S PAGE.

DUE TO WORSENING STORM CONDITIONS, ALL "NON-ESSENTIAL" PERSONNEL MAY GO HOME EARLY.
8/18/00
© 2000 United Feature Syndicate, Inc.
THIS WILL BE THE EASIEST ROUND OF LAYOFFS EVER.

I KNOW OUR E-MAIL ADDRESSES ARE SUPPOSED TO BE OUR FIRST INITIAL PLUS OUR LAST NAME.

BUT COULD YOU MAKE AN EXCEPTION?
NO.
8/19/00
© 2000 United Feature Syndicate, Inc.

THAT BRENDA UTTHEAD IS QUITE A WHINER.

A GOOD MANAGER HIRES PEOPLE WHO ARE SMARTER THAN HE IS.
SO...YOUR BOSS IS DUMBER THAN YOU?
AND YOUR BOSS'S BOSS IS DUMBER YET?
ACCORDING TO YOUR THEORY, OUR CEO IS THE DUMBEST PERSON IN THE COMPANY.
UNLESS ALL OF YOU ARE BAD MANAGERS.
TRULY WE ARE DOOMED EITHER WAY.
THIS CONCLUDES THE MOTIVATIONAL PART OF THE MEETING.
I'D GIVE YOU A HIGH FIVE BUT I DON'T LIKE TO MOVE.

IF I HIRED YOU, HOW WOULD YOU RESPOND TO SOMETHING LIKE THIS?
I USUALLY IGNORE CHAIN LETTERS.
LET'S TRY ANOTHER.
DID YOU FINISH YOUR IN BASKET?
NO, I'LL NEED A FEW MORE APPLICANTS.
8/21/00 © 2000 United Feature Syndicate, Inc.

CATBERT: EVIL H.R. DIRECTOR
EMPLOYEES WASTE TOO MUCH TIME AT FUNERALS.

ON A RELATED NOTE, OUR HEATING COSTS ARE TOO HIGH.
8/22/00 © 2000 United Feature Syndicate, Inc.

AS A MATTER OF FACT, I WOULD MIND BEING CREMATED IN THE COMPANY FURNACE.

CATBERT: EVIL H.R. DIRECTOR
WE INCREASED THE COMPLEXITY OF YOUR PAY SLIP.

NOW YOU'LL NEVER KNOW WHEN WE RIP YOU OFF!
YEEHA! YEEHA!
8/23/00 © 2000 United Feature Syndicate, Inc.
THE ONLY PART THAT REALLY BUGS ME IS THE YEEHAS.

WOULD IT BE OKAY IF I WORKED PART TIME?
THAT DEPENDS.
WOULD YOU BE WILLING TO COME IN ON YOUR DAYS OFF TO FINISH URGENT PROJECTS?
YES
SO, BASICALLY YOU NEGOTIATED A FIFTY PERCENT PAY CUT?
8/24/00 © 2000 United Feature Syndicate, Inc.

I'M SITTIN' IN A BOX AND CHECKIN' MY STOCKS.
I MUST USE ALL MY WILLPOWER TO RESIST CHECKING EVERY TEN SECONDS.
I'M SITTIN' IN A BOX AND CHECKIN' MY STOCKS.
8/25/00 © 2000 United Feature Syndicate, Inc.

OUR NEW CORPORATE SLOGAN IS...
"THE POWER OF THE INTERNET LIES IN CONVERGING THE FUTURE WITH THE HERE AND NOW."
8/26/00 © 2000 United Feature Syndicate, Inc.

GOOSE-BUMPS?
PSORIASIS.

SO THEY REPLACED OUR COMPUTERS AND NEVER TRAINED US.
I TOLD THEM WE NEEDED A TRAINING CLASS BUT THEY IGNORED MY REQUESTS.
SO OUR COMPUTERS SIT THERE UNUSED WHILE WE DO OUR WORK THE SLOW WAY.
WHY DON'T YOU READ THE COMPUTER MANUAL?
I DON'T HAVE TIME FOR THAT!
BUT YOU HAVE TIME FOR A CLASS?
IT DOESN'T ADD UP.
I'M COLD.
YOU SHOULD TRY WEARING A COAT. THEY'RE TERRIFIC.
8/27/00 © 2000 United Feature Syndicate, Inc.

I NOW OFFER SELF-SERVICE CONSULTING.
WRITE DOWN YOUR STRATEGY AND I'LL SEND YOU MASSIVE BILLS.
© 2000 United Feature Syndicate, Inc.
8/28/00
DO YOU HAVE A CARD?
I WAS HOPING YOU'D PRINT SOME FOR ME.

SELF-SERVICE CONSULTING
I WAS HIRED BECAUSE YOU'RE ALL DUMBER THAN A CRATE OF ANVILS.
NOW, CAN ANYONE TELL ME IF YOUR OPERATIONS ARE CENTRALIZED OR DECENTRALIZED?
© 2000 United Feature Syndicate, Inc.
8/29/00
OOH! OOH! I JUST THOUGHT OF A STRATEGY!

I'M GOING TO FOLLOW TOM PETERS' ADVICE AND BECOME MY OWN BRAND.
THE PHRASE YOU'RE LEAST LIKELY TO HEAR IS, "I GOTTA GET ME SOME OF THAT."
© 2000 United Feature Syndicate, Inc.
8/30/00
DAY ONE: NOT SO GOOD.

STEP AWAY FROM THAT NETWORK SERVER!
I'M CERTIFIED!
I SUMMON THE VAST POWER OF CERTIFICATION!
WELL, THIS IS EMBARRASSING; THAT'S ALL I REMEMBER FROM THE CLASSES.
© 2000 United Feature Syndicate, Inc.
8/31/00

HA HA! YOU NEVER SHOULD HAVE LET ME GET A TECHNICAL CERTIFICATION.
I USED MY NEW POWER TO GET A BETTER JOB AT A DIFFERENT COMPANY.
TELL ME AGAIN WHY I HIRED YOU?
© 2000 United Feature Syndicate, Inc.
9/1/00

AS A MANAGER, IT'S MY JOB TO REDUCE THE TURNOVER OF OUR MOST VALUABLE EMPLOYEES...
...AND TO INCREASE TURNOVER OF OUR LEAST VALUABLE EMPLOYEES.
OW! FOR THE JILLIONTH TIME, WHO KEEPS KICKING ME?!
© 2000 United Feature Syndicate, Inc.
9/2/00

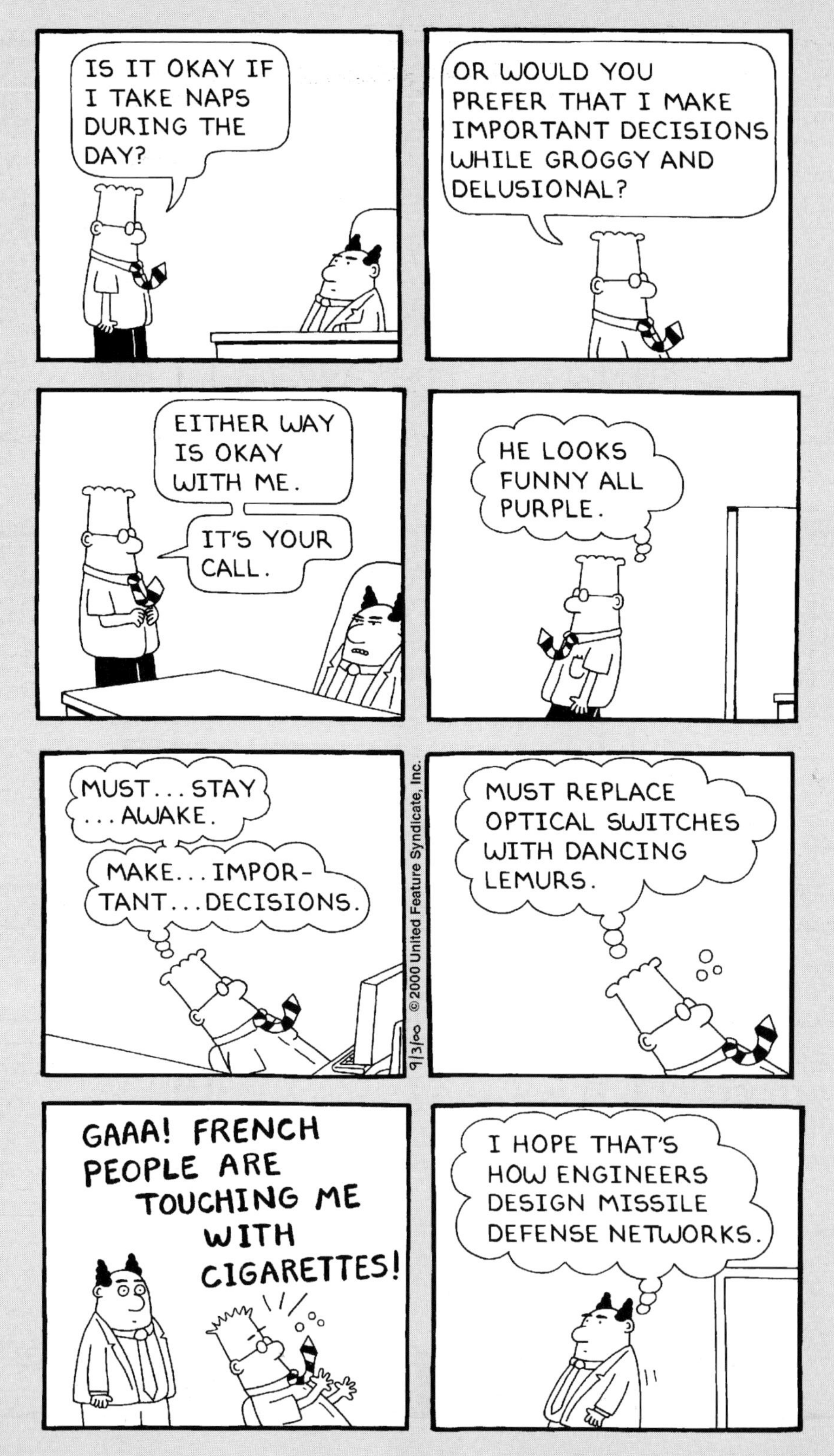
IS IT OKAY IF I TAKE NAPS DURING THE DAY?
OR WOULD YOU PREFER THAT I MAKE IMPORTANT DECISIONS WHILE GROGGY AND DELUSIONAL?
EITHER WAY IS OKAY WITH ME.
IT'S YOUR CALL.
HE LOOKS FUNNY ALL PURPLE.
MUST... STAY ... AWAKE.
MAKE... IMPOR-TANT... DECISIONS.
© 2000 United Feature Syndicate, Inc.
9/3/00
MUST REPLACE OPTICAL SWITCHES WITH DANCING LEMURS.
GAAA! FRENCH PEOPLE ARE TOUCHING ME WITH CIGARETTES!
I HOPE THAT'S HOW ENGINEERS DESIGN MISSILE DEFENSE NETWORKS.

YOUR RÉSUMÉ SAYS YOU'RE A MULTI-CELLED LIFE FORM.
THAT'S EXACTLY WHAT WE'RE LOOKING FOR!
I'M TRYING TO SHAKE HANDS. IF YOU FEEL HARASSED IN ANY WAY JUST LET OUT A YELP.
9/4/00
© 2000 United Feature Syndicate, Inc.

DILBERT, MEET THE NEW GUY.
YOU HIRED A GIANT AMOEBA?
YOU CAN'T GO AROUND JUDGING PEOPLE BY THEIR LOOKS.
WOULD YOU MIND...
TRAINING HIM?
KEEPING HIM MOIST?
9/5/00
© 2000 United Feature Syndicate, Inc.

SO, I HEAR YOU'RE A SINGLE-CELL ORGANISM.
WHAT'S UP WITH THAT?
THE NEW GUY IS ROLLING INTO A BALL AND SHEDDING WATER.
BEEN THERE.
9/6/00
© 2000 United Feature Syndicate, Inc.

THIS ISN'T WORKING OUT. I HAVE TO LET YOU GO.
MAYBE YOU CAN GET YOUR OLD JOB BACK AT FARWORKS.
GREAT. NOW HE'S GOING TO SECRETE.
9/7/00
© 2000 United Feature Syndicate, Inc.

TODAY I WILL KNOW THE JOY OF UNINTERRUPTED PRODUCTIVITY.
WE'RE FORMING A POSSE TO FIND OUT WHO LEAVES CRUMBS IN THE SINK.
I ASSUME IT'S YOU.
WE NEED MORE BLACK SHEEP AROUND HERE.
9/8/00
© 2000 United Feature Syndicate, Inc.

WORK IS FOR LOSERS.
A WINNER SAYS, "THAT'S ON MY LIST" AND NEVER COMMITS TO A DEADLINE.
WOULDN'T PEOPLE RESPECT ME LESS?
I DON'T SEE HOW.
9/9/00
© 2000 United Feature Syndicate, Inc.

I MAPPED YOUR GENOME, WALLY.
I DIDN'T KNOW THE HUMAN RESOURCES DEPARTMENT HAD THAT TECHNOLOGY.
I USED A PENCIL.
YOUR GENES PREDICT THAT YOU WILL BE A BITTER, LAZY, CAUCASIAN GUY WITH SIX HAIRS AND POOR VISION.
YOU'LL HATE CUBICLES, MEASURABLE OBJECTIVES, AND CATS WHO MAP YOUR GENOME.
©2000 United Feature Syndicate, Inc.
9/10/00
THIS IS A VIOLATION OF MY RIGHT TO PRIVACY! I'LL FIGHT IT ALL THE WAY TO THE SUPREME COURT!
NO, ACCORDING TO MY MAP, YOU'LL LOSE INTEREST AND FALL ASLEEP.
I WONDER IF THIS TECHNOLOGY WILL EVER FALL INTO THE WRONG HANDS.
ZZZZZ

NOW SIGN THIS AND THIS AND THIS.
THIS IS A MURDER CONFESSION.
IT'S FOR THE FILE.
SOMEDAY I'M GOING TO TAKE A GOOD LOOK AT THAT FILE.
9/11/00
© 2000 United Feature Syndicate, Inc.

I HID THE EMER-GENCY FLASHLIGHTS SO NO ONE CAN PLAY WITH THEM.
WHO PLAYS WITH FLASHLIGHTS? THAT'S THE DUMBEST THING I'VE EVER HEARD.
THE SHORT JEDI WILL DIE FIRST.
9/12/00
© 2000 United Feature Syndicate, Inc.

SEND
OOH!

I GET A TINY FEELING OF SELF-WORTH WHEN I SEND E-MAIL TO MY BOSS.
LOOKS LIKE SOMEONE HAS AN E-MAIL MONKEY ON HIS BACK.
I CAN QUIT WHENEVER I WANT!
9/13/00
© 2000 United Feature Syndicate, Inc.

I HAVE AN E-MAIL MONKEY ON MY BACK, BUT I CAN QUIT WHENEVER I WANT.
I DON'T NEED TO CHECK IT EVERY MINUTE. I CAN RESIST.
© 2000 United Feature Syndicate, Inc.
9/14/00
BUT LOOK! THE STUPID MONKEY HIT MY KEYBOARD WITH HIS FOOT!

CATBERT: EVIL H.R. DIRECTOR
ASOK, YOU HAVE A BAD CASE OF E-MAIL MONKEY-ON-THE-BACK.
THE ONLY CURE IS TO DEACTIVATE YOUR INTERNET CONNECTION.
© 2000 United Feature Syndicate, Inc.
9/15/00
NO PROBLEM. HEH, HEH.
HEH HEH
I KNOW YOU HAVE A PALM VII STRAPPED TO YOUR ANKLE.

I USED TO HAVE AN E-MAIL MONKEY ON MY BACK, BUT I WENT COLD TURKEY.
I STILL DO A LITTLE CHATTING BUT THAT'S NOT ADDICTIVE.
IS IT?
© 2000 United Feature Syndicate, Inc.
9/16/00
OH, JUST SHUT UP AND HOP ON.
I'M ROFL.

I DECIDED TO BECOME A BUSINESS MANAGER FOR CELEBRITIES.
WHY?
BECAUSE BANKS HAVE LOCKS.
EVERYTHING YOU OWN HAS BEEN PUT IN MY NAME..FOR...UM.. TAX PURPOSES.
YOU'RE SUCH A GOOD FRIEND.
HOW CAN I EVER REPAY YOU?
YOU CAN SIGN THIS.
IT GIVES ME THE RIGHTS TO YOUR LIFE STORY.
©2000 United Feature Syndicate, Inc.
9/17/00
IN THE UNLIKELY EVENT THAT SOME-ONE STEALS YOUR FORTUNE AND YOU BECOME A PATHETIC DRUG ADDICT...
...I CAN SELL YOUR STORY TO THE "BIOGRAPHY" CHANNEL.
THEY START FILMING ON THURSDAY.

FROM NOW ON, THIS IS GOING TO BE A FUN ORGANIZATION.
WHEN ARE YOU LEAVING?
9/18/00
© 2000 United Feature Syndicate, Inc.
I HAD NO IDEA THAT A RUBBER CHICKEN COULD HURT SO MUCH.

WHAT THE WORK-AT-HOME PERSON SAYS
DON'T DISTURB ME UNLESS THE HOUSE IS ON FIRE.
WHAT THE REST OF THE FAMILY HEARS
I AM YOUR SERVANT. MY SPECIALTY IS KILLING SPIDERS.
9/19/00
© 2000 United Feature Syndicate, Inc.
WHAT THE SPIDERS HEAR
THE HOUSE IS FULL OF WOUNDED FLIES.

THE MARKETING GUYS ARE STALLING. YOU NEED TO ESCALATE.
MUST ESCALATE.
9/20/00
© 2000 United Feature Syndicate, Inc.
I'LL NEVER UNDERSTAND HOW THIS HELPS.
SALE

CAN YOU TEST THE SOFTWARE TODAY?
NO, I'M MAKING MAJOR CHANGES TUESDAY.
YOU COULD TEST THE CURRENT VERSION.
I WISH PEOPLE WOULDN'T SLAP THEIR FOREHEADS AND SAY "AYE-YI-YI-YI" EVERY TIME I TALK.
9/21/00 © 2000 United Feature Syndicate, Inc.
THIS TO-DO LIST WILL MAKE ME MORE EFFICIENT.
I HAVE THREE FAKE EMERGENCIES, TWO DOOMED PROJECTS, FOUR UNNECESSARY MEETINGS...
I FIGURED OUT WHY YOU NEVER ASK ME HOW MY DAY WENT.
OFF YOU GO.
9/22/00 © 2000 United Feature Syndicate, Inc.

SPEED IS THE KEY TO SUCCESS.

IS IT OKAY TO DO THINGS WRONG IF WE'RE REALLY, REALLY FAST?
UM... NO.
NOW I'M ALL CONFUSED, THANK YOU VERY MUCH.
9/23/00 © 2000 United Feature Syndicate, Inc.

HALT!
YOU MOVED YOUR COMPUTER WITHOUT APPROVAL FROM THE CENTRAL CUBICLE COMMITTEE.
I WAS SIMPLY ADJUSTING THE ANGLE.
GASP
FOOL! IT WILL COST $200 FOR A TEAM OF TECHNICIANS TO MOVE IT BACK!
IT'S BETTER THIS WAY SO MY PLANT WON'T FALL OFF.
©2000 United Feature Syndicate, Inc.
9/24/00
WE HAVE GUIDE-LINES!!
I KNOW. I STAPLED THEM TO MY WALL.
YOU'D BE SURPRISED AT WHAT ISN'T ALLOWED.

DOGBERT CONSULTS
HERE'S MY REPORT FULL OF OBVIOUS GENERALITIES.
MY FEE IS $90,000.
WHAT ARE YOU RECOM-MENDING?
I RECOMMEND TELLING EVERYONE IT WAS FREE.
© 2000 United Feature Syndicate, Inc.
9/25/00

DOGBERT CONSULTS
YOU CAN REVIVE THE ENTREPRENEURIAL SPIRIT HERE BY REMINDING PEOPLE OF THE EARLY YEARS.
YOUR FOUNDERS WERE TWO BUMS WHO BEGAN IN A CARDBOARD BOX.
ONE BUM MISDIALED HIS BOOKIE AND ACCIDENTALLY BOUGHT CISCO STOCK AT THE IPO.
© 2000 United Feature Syndicate, Inc.
9/26/00

THIS NEEDS YOUR APPROVAL.
THE COMPANY WILL SAVE FORTY MILLION DOLLARS BUT YOU'LL BE TEN THOUSAND OVER BUDGET.
AND BEFORE YOU ASK, NO IT WON'T WORK THE OTHER WAY AROUND.
WHOSE SIDE ARE YOU ON?
© 2000 United Feature Syndicate, Inc.
9/27/00

I'M SURE YOUR BOSS WILL INCREASE THE BUDGET IF YOU SHOW HIM MY PLAN.
I JUST ASKED HIM FOR SOMETHING ELSE. I CAN'T KEEP ASKING HIM FOR RESOURCES!
9/28/00 © 2000 United Feature Syndicate, Inc.
SO... YOU THINK THAT DOING YOUR JOB IS A SIGN OF WEAKNESS?
LOOK WHAT IT DID TO YOU.
TED, THERE'S A HUGE DEMAND FOR EMPLOYEES LIKE YOU.
BUT NOT YOU SPECIFICALLY.
...WHICH IS FUNNY IF YOU THINK ABOUT IT.
9/29/00 © 2000 United Feature Syndicate, Inc.
HEY, IF YOU CAN'T LAUGH AT YOURSELF, WHO CAN YOU LAUGH AT?

MY STOCK OPTIONS ARE WORTH A FORTUNE NOW, YOU MISERABLE BAG OF CRUD!
OH, LOOK, THEY'RE BACK DOWN TO WORTHLESS.
9/30/00 © 2000 United Feature Syndicate, Inc.
TRY TELLING HIM THAT BAGS OF CRUD ARE HIGHLY VALUED IN SOME SOCIETIES.
SHUT UP.

WALLY, WHAT'S THE STATUS OF OUR VITAL RECORDS PROTECTION PLAN?
?
THINK FAST.
I...UH...DID EXTENSIVE INTERVIEWS WITH KEY STAKEHOLDERS.
THEN I... UH...FORMED A PLAN...
NOW ALL THE RECORDS ARE DIGITIZED AND STORED WITH 512 BIT ENCRYPTION...
...AT THE CENTER OF THE EARTH... ON NATURAL MAGNETS.
I MEANT YOU SHOULD READ THE PROJECT TEAM'S STATUS REPORT.
THEY CLAIM TO HAVE A PLAN.
LIARS.

10/1/00

THE EVIL H.R. DIRECTOR
WHAT NEW EVIL DO YOU BRING ME, UNION STEWARD STUART?
EMPLOYEES SHOULD NOT BE ALLOWED TO MOVE COMPANY COMPUTERS. THAT'S UNION WORK.
THAT'S OLD EVIL.
IT'S NEW IF WE INCLUDE PDAs AND LAPTOPS.
I LIKE THE CUT OF YOUR GIBLETS.
© 2000 United Feature Syndicate, Inc.
10/2/00

OUR NEW OFFICE BUILDING WILL BE AN ARCHITECTURAL MASTERPIECE!
THE VOICES IN MY HEAD ARE SHOUTING "NO STORAGE SPACE! NO STORAGE SPACE!"
WHAT IS HAPPENING TO ME?
IT'S CALLED EXPERIENCE.
© 2000 United Feature Syndicate, Inc.
10/3/00

DOGBERT CONSULTS
YOU NEED TO REORGANIZE BY CUSTOMER TYPE.
ONE DIVISION WOULD FOCUS ON SELLING TO FEEBLE-MINDED PEOPLE.
ARE YOU GESTURING AT ME BECAUSE I WOULD WORK IN THAT DIVISION?
WHAT'S YOUR SECOND GUESS?
© 2000 United Feature Syndicate, Inc.
10/4/00

MY PHILOSOPHY IS: MEASURE TWICE...
THEN CUT TWICE, THEN UH...
GIVE THE TAPE MEASURE A BAD PERFORMANCE REVIEW?
HEE HEE!
OOH.
10/5/00 © 2000 United Feature Syndicate, Inc.

YOUR OFFICE IS TOO FAR FROM THE EXECUTIVE OFFICES.
IT IS?
THEY ARE ACTIVELY FORGETTING YOUR NAME EVEN AS WE SPEAK. IT'S GOING...GOING...
GONE!
CAROL, WE HAVE TO MOVE MY OFFICE!
HAVE WE MET?
10/6/00 © 2000 United Feature Syndicate, Inc.

PERFORMANCE REVIEW
LASTLY, WHAT HAVE YOU DONE TO IMPROVE THE MORALE OF YOUR CO-WORKERS?
I DIDN'T GIVE THEM THE BEATINGS THEY SO RICHLY DESERVED.
I'LL SHORTEN THAT TO "TEAM PLAYER"?
10/7/00 © 2000 United Feature Syndicate, Inc.

THE INSPIRATIONAL CEO
OUR COMPANY IS TOO GOOD TO HAVE RESULTS THIS POOR.
QUESTION.
%#!* ENGINEERS.
WHAT?
ARE YOU SAYING THE LAWS OF CAUSE AND EFFECT DO NOT APPLY?
LOGICALLY, IF WE WERE GOOD, WE WOULD GENERATE GOOD RESULTS.
IS IT NOT MORE LIKELY THAT WE ARE PATHETIC LOSERS WHO GET EXACTLY WHAT WE DESERVE?
YES, INDIVIDUALLY YOU'RE ALL LOSERS. BUT TOGETHER WE'RE A GREAT COMPANY.
THANKS TO MY LEADER-SHIP.
I FEEL LIKE SQUIRMING BUT I DON'T HAVE THE ENERGY.
10/8/00 ©2000 United Feature Syndicate, Inc.

WE CAN'T PAY YOU THIS WEEK BECAUSE YOUR POSITION CODE IS MISALIGNED
WITH YOUR MODULE.
WORSE YET, NO ONE KNOWS WHAT THAT MEANS OR WHOSE RESPONSIBILITY IT IS TO FIX IT.
WHO TOLD YOU ABOUT THE PROB-LEM?
IT WAS AN ANONYMOUS NOTE WITH DISAPPEAR-ING INK.
10/9/00
© 2000 United Feature Syndicate, Inc.

I'M TRYING TO FIND SOMEONE WHO CAN HELP ME WITH A PAYROLL PROBLEM.
YOU'RE CLOSE. I'M THE GUY WHO FORWARDS YOUR CALL TO THE WRONG PERSON.
I'D LIKE TO SPEAK WITH YOUR SUPERVISOR.
I'LL FOR-WARD YOUR CALL.
10/10/00
© 2000 United Feature Syndicate, Inc.

HELEN, I'M TRANSFERRING YOU TO THE TEMPORARY ZOMBIE DIVISION.
YOU WILL BE WITH OTHER PEOPLE WHO ARE PLANNING WEDDINGS, RAISING BABIES AND DIVORCING.
SHE TOOK MY DOG.
ALL THE GOOD PLACES ARE BOOKED.
10/11/00
© 2000 United Feature Syndicate, Inc.

DO YOU WANT A STOCK TIP?
ARE YOU ASKING ME TO BELIEVE YOU'RE A LOSER AT EVERY ASPECT OF LIFE EXCEPT PICKING STOCK?
THAT'S NOT WHAT I'M ASKING.
IT'S IMPLIED.
© 2000 United Feature Syndicate, Inc.
10/12/00

HERE'S THE NEW GUY. I DON'T KNOW HIS NAME.
HE'S EITHER RUDE OR SHY. NO ONE KNOWS FOR SURE.
IF YOU FIGURE IT OUT, NAME HIM EITHER SHILO OR RUDY.
© 2000 United Feature Syndicate, Inc.
10/13/00

WHY DON'T YOU HAVE A LITTLE COFFEE WITH YOUR SUGAR, ALICE?
HEH, HEH. IT'S FUNNY BECAUSE IT'S USUALLY THE OTHER WAY AROUND.
I DON'T SEE HOW SOMETHING CAN BE FUNNY 300 TIMES BUT NOT 301 TIMES.
© 2000 United Feature Syndicate, Inc.
10/14/00

HOW DO I GET RID OF MY OLD COMPUTER?
WHY DON'T YOU GIVE IT TO A SCHOOL?
WELL, IT WOULD TAKE ME A WEEK TO FIND SOMEONE TO TAKE IT.
THE HARD DRIVE IS BROKEN AND IT HAS NO SOFTWARE.
AND IT WOULD CAUSE A TAX ACCOUNTING NIGHTMARE.
MAYBE YOU COULD LEAVE IT ON THE SCHOOL PLAYGROUND AT NIGHT.
THAT'S WHAT I DID WITH MY OLD REFRIGER-ATOR.
WHAT I HATE MOST IS THAT I DIDN'T HAVE A BETTER IDEA.
©2000 United Feature Syndicate, Inc.
10/15/00

I JUST MET WITH THE BIRDABON SOCIETY. I HAD TO PROMISE WE WON'T HURT ANY BIRDS.
OUR CATERER SERVED CHICKEN SANDWICHES FOR LUNCH.
I PRETENDED TO GIVE MINE CPR BUT I WAS REALLY EATING IT.
10/16/00 © 2000 United Feature Syndicate, Inc.
DID DILBERT DO SOMETHING TERRIBLE OR AM I HALLUCINATING?
I'D BETTER PLAY IT SAFE AND PUNISH HIM IN WAYS THAT ARE AMBIGUOUS AND UNTRACEABLE.
I HAD TO CHANGE YOUR NETWORK PASSWORD TO "DIE-DILBERT-DIE"
AND I CAN'T SAY WHY.
10/17/00 © 2000 United Feature Syndicate, Inc.

YOU NEED "DOGBERT'S DYSFUNCTIONAL EMPLOYEE RECRUIT-MENT SERVICES."
I ONLY RECRUIT EMPLOYEES WHO WERE RAISED IN DYSFUNCTIONAL FAMILIES. THEY DON'T MIND BEING MISTREATED!
HOW SOON CAN YOU GET ME SOME?
I HAVE A DOZEN IN THE TRUNK OF MY CAR.
10/18/00 © 2000 United Feature Syndicate, Inc.

I UNDERSTAND THAT YOU WERE RAISED IN A DYSFUNCTIONAL FAMILY.
YES
YOU'RE GONNA WORK SEVENTY HOURS A WEEK OR YOU'RE WORTH-LESS!!
10/19/00 © 2000 United Feature Syndicate, Inc.
YOU LOVE ME.
ARE THERE ANY MORE LIKE YOU AT HOME?
YOU'RE WORKING ME TOO HARD! I WANT TO GET HOME IN TIME TO KISS MY DAUGHTER GOODNIGHT!
AND I'M NOT THE ONLY ONE WHO FEELS THIS WAY.
10/20/00 © 2000 United Feature Syndicate, Inc.
I'VE SEEN YOUR DAUGHTER AND I'M FAIRLY CERTAIN YOU'RE THE ONLY ONE.

CATBERT: EVIL H.R. DIRECTOR
YOU THINK YOU'RE SATISFIED WITH YOUR JOB.
IN REALITY YOU'RE JUST AFRAID OF CHANGE!
10/21/00 © 2000 United Feature Syndicate, Inc.
THAT WAS SOME OF MY BEST WORK.
PURRR PURRR

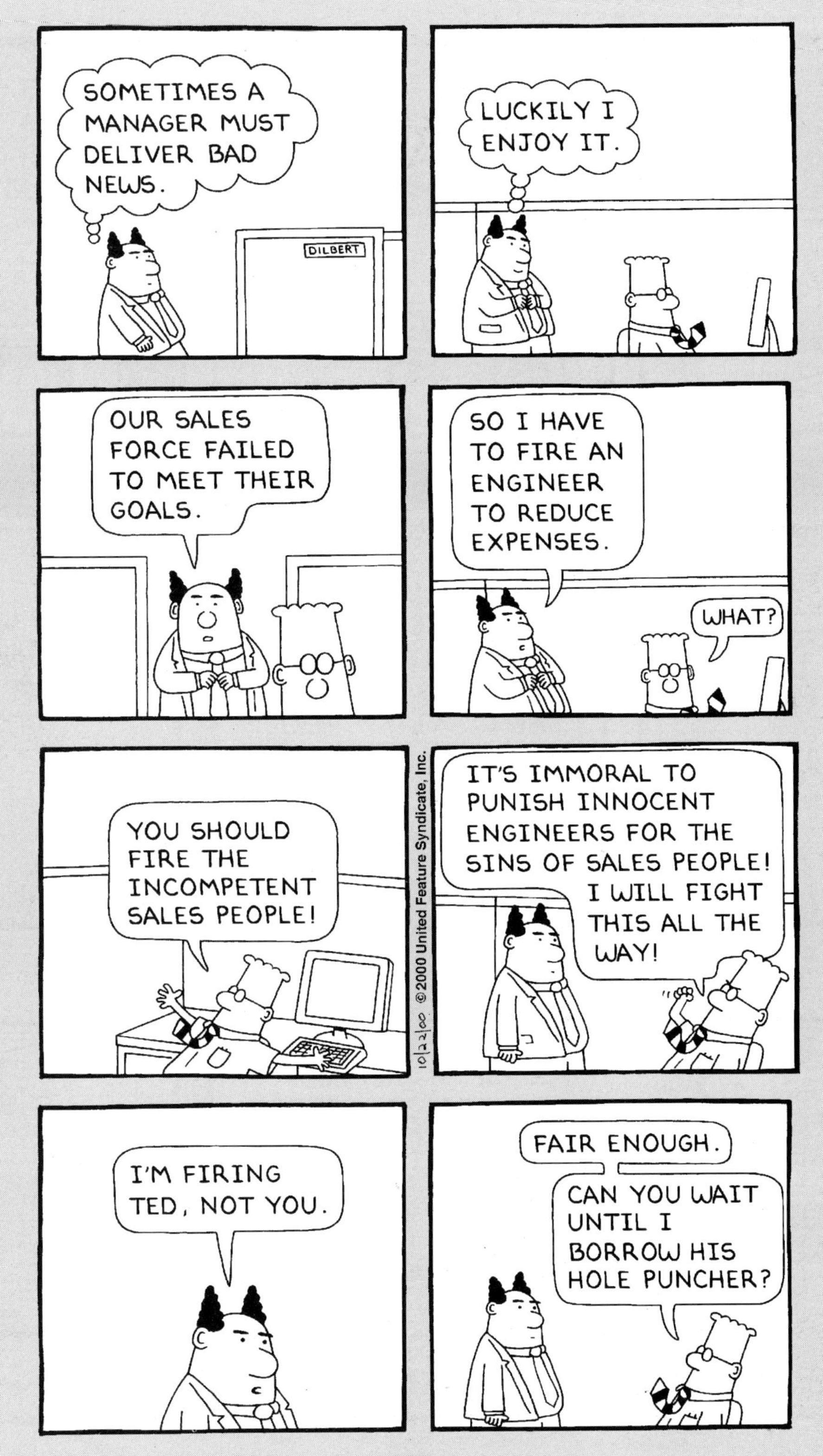
SOMETIMES A MANAGER MUST DELIVER BAD NEWS.
DILBERT
LUCKILY I ENJOY IT.
OUR SALES FORCE FAILED TO MEET THEIR GOALS.
SO I HAVE TO FIRE AN ENGINEER TO REDUCE EXPENSES.
WHAT?
YOU SHOULD FIRE THE INCOMPETENT SALES PEOPLE!
IT'S IMMORAL TO PUNISH INNOCENT ENGINEERS FOR THE SINS OF SALES PEOPLE!
I WILL FIGHT THIS ALL THE WAY!
I'M FIRING TED, NOT YOU.
FAIR ENOUGH.
CAN YOU WAIT UNTIL I BORROW HIS HOLE PUNCHER?

WHAT THE...?
YOU STILL WORK HERE?
THAT'S GONNA TAKE A BITE OUT OF MY PRODUCTIVITY.
10/23/00 © 2000 United Feature Syndicate, Inc.
YOUR PERSONAL USE OF THE INTERNET IS LIKE STEALING FROM THE COMPANY!
YOU WORK IN HUMAN RESOURCES; THAT'S LIKE STEALING FROM THE COMPANY, TOO.
MAYBE WE SHOULD FORM A GANG.
10/24/00 © 2000 United Feature Syndicate, Inc.

OUR RECORDS SHOW THAT YOU USED THE INTERNET FOR PERSONAL REASONS.
YOU'RE FIRED.
PLEASE, I MERELY ORDERED GROCERIES ONLINE SO THAT I MIGHT HAVE MORE TIME FOR WORKING.
MY MOTTO IS, YOU CAN'T SPELL "WHO CARES?" WITHOUT H.R.
IT'S EVIL, BUT IT'S TRUE.
10/25/00 © 2000 United Feature Syndicate, Inc.

I... MUST... RESIST ...USING... THE INTERNET FOR PERSONAL REASONS.
GAA! THERE'S A WHOLE WORLD OF KNOWLEDGE AND ENTERTAINMENT AT MY FINGER-TIPS... TEASING ME!
10/26/00 © 2000 United Feature Syndicate, Inc.
ICE CREAM! I'M SO HUNGRY!
NO EATING IN YOUR CUBICLE.
I FIRED EVERYONE WHO USED THE INTERNET FOR PERSONAL STUFF.
THE ONLY WRINKLE IN THAT POLICY IS THAT YOU AND I ARE THE ONLY EMPLOYEES LEFT.
10/27/00 © 2000 United Feature Syndicate, Inc.
AND FRANKLY, I USE THE WEB FOR PERSONAL STUFF TOO.
CAN YOU TEACH ME HOW?

AND WHAT'S YOUR REASON FOR LEAVING YOUR PREVIOUS JOB?
YOU FIRED ME YESTERDAY FOR NON-BUSINESS USE OF THE INTERNET.
10/28/00 © 2000 United Feature Syndicate, Inc.
CRIME DOESN'T PAY.
WAIT UNTIL YOU HEAR MY MINIMUM ACCEPTABLE SALARY.

THANK YOU. HAVE A NICE DAY.
SHE'S FLIRTING WITH ME.
UM...WOULD YOU LIKE TO GO OUT ON SATURDAY?
I WASN'T FLIRTING. THIS IS MY PHONY CUSTOMER SERVICE SMILE.
EMPLOYEES ARE REQUIRED TO SMILE.
OKAY, BUT NOW YOU'RE FLIRTING, AREN'T YOU?
NO, STILL PHONY.
WALLY HAS TO SEE THIS.
HEY, IT LOOKS LIKE SHE'S FLIRT-ING WITH ME!
IS THIS GREAT OR WHAT?

MY SON IS FLUNKING ALL HIS CLASSES. I'M HOPING HE CAN GET A JOB INVOLVING COMPUTERS.
CARRYING THEM?
10/30/00 © 2000 United Feature Syndicate, Inc.
PEOPLE DON'T LIKE IT WHEN YOU FILL IN THE BLANKS IN THEIR STORIES.

TED, YOUR THIRTY-DAY DANCE OF DEATH BEGINS TODAY.
YOU MUST FIND A NEW JOB WITHIN THE COMPANY DURING THAT TIME.
10/31/00 © 2000 United Feature Syndicate, Inc.
IS THE SPRAY-PAINT ABSOLUTELY NECESSARY?
SSSSSS
THAT'S AN "L."

I NEED A NEW JOB WITHIN THE COMPANY BEFORE THE WINDOW SHUTS.
CATBERT IS ALREADY UP TO "O." NEXT WEEK HE GETS AN "S."
WHAT'S HE SPELLING?
11/1/00 © 2000 United Feature Syndicate, Inc.
HE WOULDN'T SAY, BUT IT STARTS WITH AN "L."

CATBERT SAYS I HAVE TO GET A NEW JOB WITHIN THE COMPANY.
COULD YOU FIND IT WITHIN YOUR HEART...
I'LL CHECK.
© 2000 United Feature Syndicate, Inc.
11/2/00
NOPE. NO JOBS IN THERE.

TODAY IS MY LAST DAY. I'M SAYING MY FAREWELLS.
WE'VE NEVER TALKED, BUT I WAS WORKING MY WAY DOWN THE ROW AND HERE YOU ARE.
© 2000 United Feature Syndicate, Inc.
11/3/00
SO... LET'S STAY IN TOUCH.
DON'T BE A STRANGER.

I'VE ALWAYS BEEN AN INCURABLE ROMANTIC.
DO YOU MIND IF I TAKE OFF MY SHOE? I'VE GOT SOME SORT OF FUNGUS THAT NEEDS AIR.
© 2000 United Feature Syndicate, Inc.
11/4/00
I'M CURED!
I LIKE TO SCRATCH IT ON THE TABLE LEG.
OOPS. IS THAT YOU?

AM I FIRED?
OF COURSE NOT, TED. I ENJOY E-MAILED JOKES AS MUCH AS ANYONE.
I'M STILL LAUGHING ABOUT YOUR "TOP TEN SIGNS THAT YOUR BOSS IS A HAIRLESS RODENT".
I ASKED YOU HERE TO DISCUSS THE RECLASSIFICATION OF YOUR JOB.
STARTING TODAY, THE JOB REQUIRES A PH.D.
FEEL FREE TO APPLY FOR YOUR OWN JOB.
11/5/00 © 2000 United Feature Syndicate, Inc.
WHEW! LUCKILY, I HAVE A PH.D.
YOU DO?
WELL, THE JOB ALSO REQUIRES AN OLYMPIC GOLD MEDAL.
SYNCHRONIZED SWIMMING, 1992.
AND A POST-HUMOUS CONGRES-SIONAL MEDAL OF HONOR.

THIS SIGN IS MY PASSPORT TO CUBICLE TRAN-QUILLITY.
DO NOT DISTURB
I WONDER WHY NO ONE EVER THOUGHT OF IT BEFORE.
11/6/00 © 2000 United Feature Syndicate, Inc.
NICE SIGN. DOES IT KEEP AWAY THE UNDESIRABLES?

YOU SHOULD PUT AN "E-" IN FRONT OF YOUR TITLE.
IT'S TOO BORING JUST BEING THE DIRECTOR OF INFORMATION, OPERATIONS AND TECHNOLOGY.
11/7/00 © 2000 United Feature Syndicate, Inc.
FROM NOW ON, CALL ME THE E-DIOT.
IF ONLY THERE WERE AN EASY WAY TO REMEMBER THAT.

YOU CAN COMPENSATE FOR YOUR LACK OF KNOWLEDGE BY TALKING TOO MUCH.
AND DON'T BE LIMITED BY SOCIETY'S EXPECTATION THAT YOU BE INTERESTING.
11/8/00 © 2000 United Feature Syndicate, Inc.
SOMETIMES I LIKE TO SIT QUIETLY AND THINK UP IDEAS.
NOTHING GOOD CAN COME FROM THAT.

I'M LEARNING TO GOLF.
NOW I WON'T BE EXCLUDED FROM ALL THE MALE-DOMINATED GOLF EVENTS.
© 2000 United Feature Syndicate, Inc.
11/9/00
HAVE YOU BEEN DOMINATING GOLF EVENTS?
SOMETIMES I CAN MAKE THEM MISS PUTTS ON TV.

THANKS, HUN.
HON?!

YOU SEXIST %!*%! I WILL BURN YOUR VILLAGE AND MAKE SLAVES OF YOUR CHILDREN!
© 2000 United Feature Syndicate, Inc.
11/10/00
IT'S SHORT FOR ATTILA THE HUN. EVERYONE CALLS YOU THAT.
THAT SEEMS HARSH.

I DECLARE NEXT FRIDAY TO BE "HAWAIIAN SHIRT DAY."

HEY, YOU'RE DISGUISING PUNISHMENTS AS PERKS!
© 2000 United Feature Syndicate, Inc.
11/11/00
THEY'RE ON TO US.
DID YOU TRY THE FAKE SMILE?

I SIGNED YOU UP FOR A TRIP TO THE SOUTH POLE.
UM... WHY?
YOU'LL LOVE IT.
YOU LEAVE TOMORROW.
I AM NOT GOING TO THE SOUTH POLE!
OH, I GET IT; YOU'RE A CONTROL FREAK.
GAAA! CAN'T YOU SEE THAT IT'S YOU WHO IS TRYING TO CONTROL ME?!!
ALL I SEE IS YOU TRYING TO MANIP-ULATE ME INTO NOT SENDING YOU TO THE SOUTH POLE.
IT SEEMED EASIER.
11/12/00 ©2000 United Feature Syndicate, Inc.

WE HAVE A GIGANTIC DATABASE FULL OF CUSTOMER BEHAVIOR INFORMATION.
EXCELLENT. WE CAN USE NON-LINEAR MATH AND DATA MINING TECHNOLOGY TO OPTIMIZE OUR RETAIL CHANNELS!
11/13/00 © 2000 United Feature Syndicate, Inc.
IF THAT'S THE SAME THING AS SPAM, WE'RE HAVING A GOOD MEETING HERE.

CATBERT: EVIL H.R. DIRECTOR
WHAT'S THE MOST EVIL WAY TO USE OUR DATABASE OF CUSTOMER INFORMATION?
SHOULD WE SELL OUR MAILING LISTS, SPAM WITHOUT MERCY, OR JUST BLACK-MAIL CUSTOMERS?
11/14/00 © 2000 United Feature Syndicate, Inc.
UM... DO YOU HAVE ME IN THAT DATA-BASE?
WE KNOW ALL ABOUT YOUR CLUMPING PROBLEMS.

THE DOGBERT TEMP AGENCY USES GENETIC ENGINEERING TO GROW OUR OWN WORKERS.
ISN'T THAT DANGEROUS?
I WEAR SAFETY GOGGLES.
11/15/00 © 2000 United Feature Syndicate, Inc.
I'M THE NEW TEMP.
UM... I'M ALICE.

IT'S A PLEASURE TO MEET YOU, ALICE.
© 2000 United Feature Syndicate, Inc.
OOOWEE! THAT WAS A GOOD HAND SHAKE.
I'M FROM THE DOGBERT TEMP AGENCY. DO YOU NEED A HAND?
I GET IT. HEE HEE!
GET WHAT?
© 2000 United Feature Syndicate, Inc.
THEN I SAID, "DON'T GET MAD; TRY COUNTING TO FIFTEEN."
OUCH.

THESE COPIES YOU MADE FOR ME ARE BLANK.
THAT'S BECAUSE ALL THE ORIGINALS WERE BLANK.
© 2000 United Feature Syndicate, Inc.
MAYBE YOU COULD HAVE CHECKED THE OTHER SIDES.
TALK TO THE HAND.

I'M WRITING A BUSINESS BOOK CALLED "CHANGE HAPPENS. GET OVER IT."
THE TITLE SAYS IT ALL.
YEAH, IT NEEDS FILLER.
HOW ABOUT A PARABLE?
GOOD IDEA.
TWO BULLS WERE TALKING.
ONE BULL SAYS, "I'M AFRAID OF CHANGE."
THE OTHER BULL SAYS, "GET OVER IT."
LATER THAT DAY THEY WERE BOTH GROUND INTO HAMBURGERS AND SERVED AT A PICNIC.
THE HARD PART WILL BE FINDING SOMEONE TO WRITE THE FOREWORD.
11/19/00
© 2000 United Feature Syndicate, Inc.

ALL MUSIC ON THE INTERNET SHOULD BE FREE. ARTISTS COULD MAKE MONEY FROM DIGITAL TIPS.
GREAT IDEA. WE'LL DO THE SAME THING HERE WITH THE ENGINEERS.
HAVE YOU EVER NOTICED THAT MY IDEAS ARE ONLY BRILLIANT WHEN APPLIED TO OTHER PEOPLE?
11/20/00 © 2000 United Feature Syndicate, Inc.

MY NAME IS WALLY AND I'LL BE YOUR ENGINEER.
OUR SPECIAL TODAY IS INCOMPREHENSIBLE MUMBLING IN AN ACRONYM SAUCE WITH A SNIDE OF ATTITUDE.
I'LL JUST HAVE A TECHNICAL REVIEW.
DO YOU WANT SARCASM WITH THAT?
11/21/00 © 2000 United Feature Syndicate, Inc.

I HATE WORKING FOR TIPS.
NO, I ORDERED THE R.F.P.
MAYBE YOU WERE THINKING R.F.P. BUT YOU SAID SPEC BINDER, YOU ARROGANT COW!
WITH ANY LUCK, SHE'LL SAY, "YOU HAD ME AT COW."
11/22/00 © 2000 United Feature Syndicate, Inc.

HOW MUCH DID YOU MAKE IN TIPS TODAY?
THREE BREATH MINTS AND ONE DEATH THREAT SCRAWLED ON A NAPKIN.
11/23/00 © 2000 United Feature Syndicate, Inc.
I HOPE I DON'T FORGET WHICH BREATH MINT CAME FROM THE NAPKIN GUY.
DILBERT, MY MAN, YOU'RE STAYIN' REAL AND KEEPIN' TO THE CORE.
IS THAT GOOD?
I DON'T EVEN KNOW WHAT IT MEANS.
11/24/00 © 2000 United Feature Syndicate, Inc.
WHY DO YOU SAY THINGS THAT HAVE NO MEANING?
DU-U-U-DE!
I USED TO NOT CARE ABOUT MY SUBORDINATES.
BUT THAT'S ALL CHANGED.
11/25/00 © 2000 United Feature Syndicate, Inc.
NOW I DELEGATE THE NOT-CARING FUNCTION TO WHAT'S-HER-FACE OVER HERE.

MY ANALYSIS SHOWS THAT YOUR PET PROJECT ISN'T FEASIBLE.
TRY WORKING THE NUMBERS.
THAT WOULDN'T CHANGE THE UNDERLYING REALITY.
WHAT IF WE MASSAGED THE NUMBERS?
MASSAGING THE NUMBERS MEANS THE SAME THING AS WORKING THE NUMBERS.
YOU CAN'T MAKE THE IMPOSSIBLE POSSIBLE BY HALLUCINATING NEW NUMBERS.
DO YOU HAVE ANY OTHER IDEAS?
THAT DEPENDS ON WHAT THE PHRASE "FIDDLE WITH THE NUMBERS" MEANS.
11/26/00 © 2000 United Feature Syndicate, Inc.

WALLY, WE CAN'T FIND OUR CPR DUMMY. I NEED YOUR HELP.
FINDING IT?
11/27/00
© 2000 United Feature Syndicate, Inc.
YES, ASSUMING YOU CAN DO THAT WHILE LYING ON YOUR BACK WITH YOUR MOUTH OPEN.
THE COMPANY WILL BE HOLDING MAN-DATORY CPR TRAINING FOR ALL EMPLOYEES.
GAA!!
I AM SURROUNDED BY PEAR-SHAPED, BEEF-EATING, MIDDLE-AGED MEN WHO I PREFER NOT TO TOUCH.
11/28/00
© 2000 United Feature Syndicate, Inc.
UH-OH... I HOPE THAT'S JUST STRESS.

ASOK IS DOWN. DOES ANYONE KNOW CPR?
IS CPR THE ONE WHERE WE TAKE HIS KIDNEY AND LEAVE HIM IN A TUB OF ICE?
11/29/00
© 2000 United Feature Syndicate, Inc.
UM... I DON'T THINK SO.
WE'D BETTER STRIP HIM AND SHAVE HIM JUST IN CASE.

OKAY, WE HAVE ONE VOTE FOR USING CPR, ONE VOTE FOR THE HEIMLICH MANEUVER . . .
AND TWO VOTES FOR SNEAKING UP BEHIND HIM AND YELLING "BOO."
I DON'T SEE HOW WE CAN GET BEHIND HIM.
WHAT IF WE DRILL A HOLE FROM BELOW?
© 2000 United Feature Syndicate, Inc.
11/30/00

I'LL SEE IF THE GUYS IN MARKETING KNOW FIRST AID.
REALLY? I PICKED THAT INTERN IN OUR ENGINEERING DEAD POOL!
APPARENTLY OUR TEAM-BUILDING POTLUCK LUNCH DIDN'T TAKE.
© 2000 United Feature Syndicate, Inc.
12/1/00

I'M ALIVE!
WHICH ONE OF YOU ANGELS ADMINISTERED THE LIFE-SAVING CPR?
SPEAKING OF "LIFESAVERS," I COULD SURE USE ONE RIGHT NOW.
© 2000 United Feature Syndicate, Inc.
12/2/00

I'D LIKE TO WORK FLEX TIME.
I'LL WORK FOR FIVE HOURS BEFORE ANYONE ELSE GETS TO THE OFFICE...
THEN I'LL TAKE A BREAK FOR TEN HOURS...
THEN I'LL WORK FIVE MORE HOURS AFTER THE WITNESSES... ER...CO-WORKERS GO HOME.
YOU'LL KNOW I'M WORKING HARD BECAUSE MY CUBICLE WILL BE FILTHY.
BUT I HAVE TO BE PERFECTLY HONEST; THERE'S A DOWN SIDE TO THIS PLAN.
I WOULD MISS YOUR STAFF MEETINGS THAT I CHERISH SO MUCH.
I'M HAVING TROUBLE KEEPING MY CLEVER SCHEMES SEPARATE FROM MY SARCASM.
12/3/00
©2000 United Feature Syndicate, Inc.

AAHH, ONE SWEET WEEK AWAY FROM MY JOB.
JURY ROOM
I'LL HAVE HOURS OF QUIET TIME TO READ MY NEW BOOK.

12/4/00 © 2000 United Feature Syndicate, Inc.
YADDA YADDA BLAH BLAH
THERE'S A GUY HERE WITH A BOOK.
BLAH YADDA
BLAH BLAH
YACK YACK

JURY DUTY
WHAT EXCUSE ARE YOU PLANNING TO USE?
I'M HAPPY TO SERVE. IT'S MY CIVIC RESPONSIBILITY.
12/5/00 © 2000 United Feature Syndicate, Inc.
INSANITY; GOOD ONE.

JURY SELECTION
JUROR EIGHT, DO YOU HAVE ANY MEDICAL PROBLEMS THAT WOULD PREVENT YOU FROM SERVING?

NO, I NEED JURY DUTY.
12/6/00 © 2000 United Feature Syndicate, Inc.
WOULD IT BE FAIR TO SAY YOU DON'T KNOW WHAT YOU NEED?
WHY DOES EVERYONE ASK ME THAT?

JURY SELECTION
YOUR HONOR, IT IS AGAINST MY RELIGION TO JUDGE OTHERS. ONLY GOD MAY JUDGE.
YOU'RE EXCUSED.
12/7/00 © 2000 United Feature Syndicate, Inc.
OOH OOH! I JUST CHANGED MY RELIGION!
JERK

MY CLIENT'S LIFE NOW RESTS IN YOUR CAPABLE HANDS.
ZZZZ ZZZZZ ZZZZZ ZZZ
12/8/00 © 2000 United Feature Syndicate, Inc.
JURY DELIBERATIONS
DID ANYTHING HAPPEN AFTER "PLEASE RISE"?

THE JURY VERDICT
WE FIND THE DEFENDANT GUILTY...
...OF THIS CRIME AND MAYBE A FEW OTHERS THAT DIDN'T COME UP.
12/9/00 © 2000 United Feature Syndicate, Inc.
LASTLY, DO YOU HAVE ANY BROCHURES FOR THE WITNESS PROTECTION PROGRAM?

AND WE'LL HAVE SUB-SECOND RESPONSE TIME.
ACTUALLY, IT'S ALREADY TWO SECONDS, AND YOUR CHANGE WILL ADD TWO MORE.
WHY DO YOU ALWAYS HAVE TO BE RIGHT?!
JUST ONCE CAN'T YOU ADMIT I'M RIGHT?
OKAY, I ADMIT THAT TWO PLUS TWO EQUALS LESS THAN ONE.
I DON'T MEAN NOW, JERK. I MEAN IN GENERAL.
OKAY. IN GENERAL I ADMIT THAT THE RULES OF PHYSICS ARE OPTIONAL.
YOU'RE DOING IT WRONG!!
YOU'RE RIGHT. MY FAULT AGAIN.
12/10/00 ©2000 United Feature Syndicate, Inc.

WE DON'T HAVE ENOUGH ENGINEERS TO HANDLE ALL THE REQUESTS FOR SALES SUPPORT.
BUILD AN ONLINE DATABASE TO LOG ALL THE REQUESTS.
12/11/00 © 2000 United Feature Syndicate, Inc.
IT MIGHT LOOK AS IF I'M STARING AT YOU WITH A MIXTURE OF CONTEMPT AND DIS-BELIEF, BUT I'M ACTUALLY MEDITATING.

IS THAT WHAT YOU WANTED?
I'M NOT SAYING.
IF I TELL YOU IT'S GOOD, YOU'LL RUB IT IN MY FACE AT YOUR PERFORMANCE REVIEW.
12/12/00 © 2000 United Feature Syndicate, Inc.
I'M SORRY.
SEE HOW YOU ARE?

DOGBERT CONSULTS
I'VE BEEN TOLD TO MAKE A SUCCESSION PLAN.
THE PLAN SHOULD SAY WHAT TO DO IF I DIE.
I CAN HELP.
12/13/00 © 2000 United Feature Syndicate, Inc.
AND IF SATAN MAKES YOU STAND IN FLAMING WORMS UP TO YOUR NOSE, TRY STANDING ON YOUR TIPTOES FOR ETERNITY.

THE SUCCESSION PLAN
IF ANYTHING HAPPENS TO ME, WALLY WILL BE YOUR LEADER.
?
I HAVE A MULTI-VITAMIN! QUICK, TAKE IT!
© 2000 United Feature Syndicate, Inc.
12/14/00
WE'RE SAFE FOR NOW.
THIS TURNED OUT TO BE A MIXED BLESSING.

WHY DID YOU CROSS-CHARGE YOUR TIME TO MY BUDGET?
I ATTENDED YOUR MEET-ING.
ALL YOU DID WAS SIT THERE LIKE A DRUNKEN MONKEY. I WANT A REFUND.
TALK TO MY BOSS.
© 2000 United Feature Syndicate, Inc.
12/15/00
...SO IT DOESN'T SEEM FAIR.
KA-CHING!

ARE THERE ANY QUESTIONS?
© 2000 United Feature Syndicate, Inc.
12/16/00
DO YOU EVER FEEL ALONE WHEN YOU'RE WITH PEOPLE?
I TRY TO.

EVERYTHING IS READY. WE JUST NEED THE BUDGET.
YOU DID GET THE FUNDING...
DIDN'T YOU?
I'VE BEEN VERY BUSY.
THIS PROJECT HAS BEEN YOUR TOP PRIORITY FOR OVER A YEAR!!!
YOU ONLY HAD ONE TASK: GET FUNDING.
WHAT HAVE YOU BEEN DOING FOR THE PAST YEAR?!
12/17/00 © 2000 United Feature Syndicate, Inc.
I REMEMBER ATTENDING MEETINGS...
AAY-III-YIII-YIII!!
IF YOU NEED ANYTHING, JUST HOLLER.

I WORRY THAT CASUAL DRESS DAYS ENCOURAGE FLIRTA- TIOUS BEHAVIOR.
I MEAN, LOOK HOW ADORABLE I AM IN MY TURTLENECK SWEATER. HOW ARE THE LADIES SUPPOSED TO CONCENTRATE?
12/18/00 © 2000 United Feature Syndicate, Inc.
DO YOU THINK I SHOULD PUT WARNING CONES AROUND MY CUBICLE?

CASUAL DRESS DAY IS HURTING OUR PRODUCTIVITY. WE NEED TO CANCEL IT.
IS IT POSSIBLE THAT OUR REAL PROBLEMS ARE CAUSED BY IRRATIONAL MANAGEMENT?
12/19/00 © 2000 United Feature Syndicate, Inc.
NO, I THINK COMFORTABLE PANTS ARE THE PROBLEM.
SOUNDS RIGHT.

THERE WILL BE NO MORE CASUAL DRESS DAYS.
WE BELIEVE THAT EMPLOYEES WORK HARDER WHEN THEY ARE WEARING UNCOMFORTABLE CLOTHES.
12/20/00 © 2000 United Feature Syndicate, Inc.
I FEEL ALL MOTIVATED BUT I CAN'T LIFT MY ARMS.

I'M THINKING OF ADOPTING AN INCOMPREHENSIBLE ACCENT SO PEOPLE WON'T ASK ME QUESTIONS.
UM... ARE YOU LEAVING THAT COFFEE POT EMPTY RIGHT IN FRONT OF ME?
MEEYERNA DERNA FURNA ALGONKIN BUHJOORNA.
12/21/00 © 2000 United Feature Syndicate, Inc.

WALLY, ARE YOU FREE FOR LUNCH?
I NEED TO REMIND MYSELF HOW LUCKY I AM THAT I DON'T HAVE YOUR LAZINESS OR PERSONALITY OR LOOKS.
WOULD YOU SAY I'M KIND OF A RENAISSANCE LOSER?
12/22/00 © 2000 United Feature Syndicate, Inc.

AS YOU KNOW, I'M THE ONLY EMPLOYEE WHO IS NOT EXCEEDING EXPECTATIONS.
YOU SHOULD PUNISH THE OTHERS FOR UNSCRUPULOUSLY PADDING THEIR OBJECTIVES!
THOSE LYING WEASELS!!
CAN I GET A WHISTLE-BLOWER AWARD FOR THIS?
12/23/00 © 2000 United Feature Syndicate, Inc.

I'VE BEEN THINKING ABOUT YOUR BIRTH-DAY, MOM.
HOW SWEET.
IT SEEMS SO INEFFICIENT TO WRAP UP YOUR PRESENT.
YOU'LL JUST RIP UP THE WRAPPING PAPER AN HOUR LATER.
SO I WAS THINKING OF THROWING A TOWEL OVER IT INSTEAD.
YOU'D GET ALL OF THE ELEMENT OF SURPRISE WITHOUT WASTING PAPER.
MAYBE I CAN USE ONE OF YOUR TOWELS SO I DON'T HAVE TO LUG ONE FROM MY HOUSE.
OF COURSE, DEAR. I WOULDN'T WANT YOU TO LUG A BIG HEAVY TOWEL JUST FOR ME.
GOOD. IT'S SETTLED.
THOSE AREN'T FOR YOU.

I MUST CLEAR MY MIND OF ALL THOUGHTS.
AT THE END OF THE DAY WE'LL BE IN A MARKET SPACE ON A GOING FORWARD BASIS.
12/25/00 © 2000 United Feature Syndicate, Inc.
OM... OM... PAGE...
I'LL COME BACK WHEN YOU'RE DONE PRACTICING BEING USELESS.
I THINK HE TRIED TO MEDITATE.
THAT'S THE PROBLEM.
YOU SHOULDN'T MIX MEDITATION WITH MANAGEMENT. THE MIND GETS TOO EMPTY.
12/26/00 © 2000 United Feature Syndicate, Inc.
WHAT CAN WE DO?
I PLAN TO RIFLE THROUGH HIS POCKETS.

HE MIGHT BE FAKING A COMA TO AVOID WORK.

THE ONLY WAY TO FIND OUT IS TO PUNCH HIM REPEATEDLY.
12/27/00 © 2000 United Feature Syndicate, Inc.
MAYBE WE SHOULD GET ALICE.
DO YOU REMEMBER IF I'M RIGHT- OR LEFT-HANDED?

I'LL TAPE A PENCIL TO HIS HAND AND USE IT TO SIGN OFF ON A RAISE FOR ME.
THAT WOULD BE SO UNETHICAL...
HICCUP
MAY I HAVE TEN PERCENT?
12/28/00 © 2000 United Feature Syndicate, Inc.
THAT HICCUP DAMAGED MY MORAL COMPASS.
A MANAGER'S BRAIN IS LIKE A PUMP. IF IT BECOMES EMPTY YOU MUST PRIME IT.
WHATEVER HE LEARNS FIRST WILL FORM THE FOUNDATION FOR ALL OF HIS FUTURE PERCEPTIONS.
12/29/00 © 2000 United Feature Syndicate, Inc.
THIS GUY HAS BEEN TALKING SMACK ABOUT YOU.
UNH...

I ASKED FOR MORE E-MAIL STORAGE SPACE AND YOU DELETED ALL OF MY FILES!
YOU COMPLAIN WHEN I IGNORE YOUR REQUESTS AND YOU COMPLAIN WHEN I DELETE YOUR FILES.
12/30/00 © 2000 United Feature Syndicate, Inc.
THOSE AREN'T YOUR ONLY CHOICES!!
I CAN'T PLEASE EVERYONE.

ANY ADVICE?
TRY TO BE LESS LIKE YOU.
THAT MIGHT WORK.
LESS LIKE ME...LESS LIKE ME.
I COLLECT CRYSTALS.
UH-OH.
I DON'T KNOW OF ANY SCIENTIFIC EVIDENCE THAT THEY CAN HEAL.
WHEW.
BUT IT'S MY POINT OF VIEW THAT THEY DO.
WHEN DID IGNORANCE BECOME A POINT OF VIEW?
TOO MUCH LIKE ME.
12/31/00 ©2000 United Feature Syndicate, Inc.

DILBERT, MEET TOPPER. HE'S AMAZING.
NO MATTER WHAT YOU SAY ABOUT YOURSELF, HE'LL TOP IT.
© 2000 United Feature Syndicate, Inc.
1/1/01
HOW ARE YOU?
I CAN'T GO FIRST. IT RUINS MY SYSTEM.
I'M GETTING A MOUSE CRAMP.
I SPENT SEVEN YEARS CHAINED UPSIDE DOWN TO AN ELBONIAN PRISON WALL.
© 2000 United Feature Syndicate, Inc.
1/2/01
AT THE RISK OF SOUNDING TOO COMPETITIVE, I BELIEVE I'M WINNING THIS CONVERSATION.

MY PROJECT WILL SAVE THE COMPANY A MILLION DOLLARS.
MINE SAVES TWENTY MILLION.

MY PROJECT WILL TAKE A YEAR TO COMPLETE.
MINE TAKES A WEEK.
© 2000 United Feature Syndicate, Inc.
1/3/01
TOPPER, I HAVE HALF A MIND...
I HAVE ONE PERCENT OF A MIND.

MY HEAD-ACHE IS A DOOZY.
HA! THAT'S NOTHING.
BAM! BAM! BAM!
UM... YOU WIN.
I'M JUST GETTING STARTED!
1/4/01 © 2000 United Feature Syndicate, Inc.

I CREATED SOFTWARE THAT MAKES ALL COPYRIGHTED WORK ON THE NET AVAIL-ABLE FOR FREE!
WOULDN'T THAT DESTROY ALL FORMS OF CREATIVITY AND PLUNGE US INTO A DEPRESSION?
YES... BUT IT IS VERY NEAT.
1/5/01 © 2000 United Feature Syndicate, Inc.

MY PLAN IS TO GIVE AWAY OUR PRODUCT FOR FREE.
WE'LL ONLY BILL CUSTOMERS WHO ASK US TO DEINSTALL IT.
FOR ONCE, THOSE REPORTS OF CONSUMER DECAPITATIONS WILL WORK IN OUR FAVOR.
1/6/01 © 2000 United Feature Syndicate, Inc.

NO KNOWN BATTERY TECHNOLOGY CAN HANDLE THIS LOAD AND BE THIS SIZE.
THAT'S NOT WHAT YOU WANTED TO HEAR.
SO YOUR MIND WILL ERASE WHAT I SAID...
...AND REPLACE THE MEMORY WITH SOMETHING TOTALLY RIDICULOUS SO YOU CAN QUESTION MY MOTIVES.
THE TRANS-FORMATION IS COMPLETE.
GAAH!
HOW CAN YOU SAY THERE'S NO SUCH THING AS A BATTERY?!
YOU'RE LYING TO AVOID WORK! I'M GOING TO TALK TO YOUR BOSS!
LATELY, THE ONLY THING KEEPING ME FROM BEING A SERIAL KILLER IS MY DISTASTE FOR MANUAL LABOR.
YOU'RE PREACH-ING TO THE CHOIR.
1/7/01 ©2001 United Feature Syndicate, Inc.

DO YOU HAVE A PLAN FOR RETAINING THE BEST EMPLOYEES?
I WHITTLE AT THEIR CONFIDENCE UNTIL THEY BELIEVE NO ONE ELSE WOULD EVER HIRE THEM.
© 2001 United Feature Syndicate, Inc.
1/8/01
DOESN'T THAT MAKE THEM SLUG-GISH?
YES, BUT IF THEY'RE ALL SLUGGISH, IT LOOKS RIGHT.
HELLO, EMPLOYEE. I'M THE MOTIVATION FAIRY.
MY MAGIC WAND WILL MAKE YOU ENJOY WORKING DESPITE THE UTTER FUTILITY.
© 2001 United Feature Syndicate, Inc.
1/9/01
KNOCK YOUR-SELF OUT.
WALLY?! GAA! I THOUGHT YOU WERE A MYTH!

THE MOTIVATION FAIRY
YOU WILL BE MY GREATEST CHALLENGE.
I'LL BET YOU GET PAID LESS THAN MINIMUM WAGE AND THEY DON'T REIM-BURSE YOU FOR TRAVEL.
© 2001 United Feature Syndicate, Inc.
1/10/01
WINGS... SO... HEAVY...
SO, WHAT KIND OF CAREER PATH YOU GOT GOING?

THE MOTIVATION FAIRY
IF YOU WORK HARD, YOU WILL GAIN THE RESPECT OF YOUR PEERS.
IF I AVOID THE STRESS OF HARD WORK, I WILL OUT-LIVE MY PEERS.
© 2001 United Feature Syndicate, Inc.
HARD WORK CAN KILL ME?
IF YOU'RE LUCKY.

THE MOTIVATION FAIRY
IT SEEMS LIKE YOUR JOB ISN'T VERY RE-WARDING.
VISION GETTING BLURRY.
LONG HOURS. NO RAISES. NO CUBICLE.
HAIR COMING OUT IN CLUMPS.
© 2001 United Feature Syndicate, Inc.
HE'S GOOD. HE'S VERY GOOD.

IF YOU WORK HARD, YOU CAN ACHIEVE GREAT THINGS!
AND THEN YOU DIE.
© 2001 United Feature Syndicate, Inc.
IT NEVER PAYS TO MIX REALITY WITH INSPIR-ATIONAL SPEECHES.

I HAVE THE RESULTS OF THE EMPLOYEE PERSONALITY TYPE PREFERENCES.
REMIND ME AGAIN WHY WE'RE DOING THIS.
YOUR TEAMWORK WILL BE BETTER WHEN YOU UNDERSTAND THAT YOU HAVE DIFFERENT STYLES OF THINKING.
FOR EXAMPLE, DILBERT PREFERS TO USE LOGIC TO SOLVE PROBLEMS.
BUT RANDY RELIES MORE HEAVILY ON MORALS AND VALUES TO SOLVE PROBLEMS.
1/14/01 ©2001 United Feature Syndicate, Inc.
THAT SOUNDS LIKE A FANCY WAY OF SAYING RANDY IS AN IDIOT.
OH, YEAH? WELL, I MIGHT BE AN IDIOT BUT YOU'RE ILLOGICAL.
THAT DIDN'T SOUND AS MENACING AS I HAD HOPED.
IT'S OKAY.
WE UNDER-STAND.

I'D LIKE YOU TO MEET OUR AD AGENCY'S CREATIVE TEAM.
PETE PETERS, ROBERT ROBERTS, AND HOLLY HOLLISTER.
WITTY REMARK, ANYONE?
I'VE GOT NOTHING.
© 2001 United Feature Syndicate, Inc.
1/15/01

THE AD AGENCY
THIS CAT WILL SAY SOMETHING.
THEN THIS OTHER CAT WILL SAY, "YEAH, RIGHT."
IT'S LIKE SARCASM.
HA HA HA HA HA HA HA!
THIS EXPLAINS SO MUCH.
© 2001 United Feature Syndicate, Inc.
1/16/01

THE AD AGENCY
THE STICK MAN RUNS THROUGH A TIRE FIRE AND GETS EATEN BY A GIANT WOLVERINE.
WILL THAT MAKE PEOPLE LIKE US?
IT'S NOT AN EXACT SCIENCE.
© 2001 United Feature Syndicate, Inc.
1/17/01

THE AD AGENCY
IS IT WISE TO INSULT ALL OF THESE MINORITY GROUPS IN OUR COMMERCIAL?
WHAT'S THE WORST THING THAT COULD HAPPEN?
DOES OUR COMPANY HAVE TO SPIT ON A FLAG?
THAT'S IT; YOU'RE ON MY "DIFFICULT CLIENT" LIST NOW.
© 2001 United Feature Syndicate, Inc.
1/18/01

THE "EXACTLY" MAN
YOUR IDEA WON'T WORK. NO ONE WOULD BUY THIS KIND OF PRODUCT.
WE ALREADY SELL TEN MILLION OF THESE PER YEAR. MY IDEA JUST MAKES THEM BETTER.
EXACTLY!!
?
© 2001 United Feature Syndicate, Inc.
1/19/01

THE "EXACTLY" MAN
EVERYTHING YOU SAID IN THE MEETING WAS WRONG. HERE'S THE PROOF.

EXACTLY!!
OKAY, I'M NOT EVEN SURE THAT WAS A HUMANOID RESPONSE.
© 2001 United Feature Syndicate, Inc.
1/20/01

PROFESSIONAL LIAR
WHAT KIND OF LIE DO YOU NEED?
IT'S. . . IT'S EMBARRASS-ING.
ARE YOU A PRODUCER WHO NEEDS A GOOD REVIEW FOR A LOUSY MOVIE?
NO.
ARE YOU AN AUTHOR WHO NEEDS A SLOBBERING QUOTE FOR THE COVER OF YOUR LOUSY BOOK?
IT'S WORSE THAN THAT.
MUCH WORSE.
1/21/01 ©2001 United Feature Syndicate, Inc.
WORSE?
THAT COULD ONLY BE . . .
AAACK!
FIND SOMEONE ELSE, YOU FILTHY DOT-COM FOUNDER! I HAVE MY LIMITS!
. . . AND SINCE YOUR FIRM UNDERWROTE OUR IPO . . .
WOULD I GET TO BE ON TV?

UM...MORDAC, MY NEW PC ARRIVED WITHOUT A MONITOR.
BAH! ONLY INTERNS WITH WEAK MEMORIES NEED MONITORS!
1/22/01 © 2001 United Feature Syndicate, Inc.
PLEASE. I AM HAVING ENOUGH DIFFICULTY MEMORIZING MY CALENDAR.
DID YOU WANT ANY CHEESE WITH THAT WHINE?
I'M GOING TO START UP A DISCOUNT BROKERAGE FIRM.
I'LL OFFER MY LOWEST COMMISSIONS TO CUSTOMERS WHO DON'T MIND BAD ADVICE AND VERBAL ABUSE.
1/23/01 © 2001 United Feature Syndicate, Inc.
DID I MENTION THAT I WON'T BE KEEPING ANY RECORDS?
YOU DIDN'T NEED TO.

DISCOUNT BROKERAGE
YOU CAN ONLY OPEN AN ACCOUNT IF YOU MEET MY STRINGENT REQUIRE-MENTS.
TRUE OR FALSE: MONEY EVAPORATES BECAUSE OF PHOTO-SYNTHESIS.
TRUE?
1/24/01 © 2001 United Feature Syndicate, Inc.
YOU'RE IN.
DON'T YELL YEE-HAW!

DISCOUNT BROKERAGE
I NEED AN ESTATE PLAN FOR AFTER I PASS AWAY.
HERE'S A PLAN: STAY DEAD. NO ONE LIKES A ZOMBIE.
© 2001 United Feature Syndicate, Inc.
WHAT ABOUT GIFTS?
ZOMBIES MAKE BAD GIFTS.

DISCOUNT BROKERAGE
WHEN YOU OPEN AN ACCOUNT, YOU'LL GET A FREE DART BOARD AND A MONKEY.
IF YOUR BALANCE DROPS BELOW FIVE HUNDRED DOLLARS, WE'LL ORDER THE MONKEY TO KILL YOU.
© 2001 United Feature Syndicate, Inc.
WELL, THINK ABOUT IT AND GET BACK TO ME.

DISCOUNT BROKERAGE
CAN YOU GIVE ME FREE INVESTMENT ADVICE?
SURE
GIVE ME ALL OF YOUR MONEY NOW NOW NOW!!
© 2001 United Feature Syndicate, Inc.
WHAT IF I PAID FOR SOME ADVICE?
IT'S THE SAME EXCEPT MY EARS DON'T FLIP UP IN A THREATENING MANNER.

WE'VE GOT TO FIGURE OUT WHY ALL OUR PROJECTS FAIL.
WHAT DO ALL OUR PROJECTS HAVE IN COMMON?
IT MIGHT NOT BE OBVIOUS.
BUT IF WE'RE HONEST WITH OURSELVES...
WE CAN FIND THE SOURCE OF THE PROBLEM.
AH-AH AH-
SCRATCH SCRATCH
1/28/01 ©2001 United Feature Syndicate, Inc.
ACH-ITZ-YOU!!
GESUNDHEIT
SO, DOES ANYONE KNOW WHAT THE PROBLEM IS?
I'VE NOTICED THAT DILBERT DOESN'T WORK AS HARD AS I THINK HE SHOULD.

YOUR STOCK WILL RISE IF A STOCK ANALYST SAYS GOOD THINGS ABOUT YOUR COMPANY.
HOW IS THAT EVEN POSSIBLE?
ONE WORD: WEASELS.
I JUST FOUND MY NEW PICK-AND-SHOVEL CORE HOLDING.
1/29/01 © 2001 United Feature Syndicate, Inc.

EQUITY ANALYST
I'LL RATE YOUR STOCK A "MUST BUY NOW" IF YOU GIVE US YOUR INVESTMENT BANKING BUSINESS.
AREN'T YOU SUPPOSED TO HAVE A CHINESE WALL BETWEEN THOSE TWO BUSINESSES?
AM I TOO EARLY?
USE THE DOOR, IDIOT.
1/30/01 © 2001 United Feature Syndicate, Inc.

WE OUTSOURCED OUR SALES AND FULFILLMENT FUNCTIONS TO AN ELBONIAN COMPANY.
UM...ARE YOU SURE THAT'S THE BEST WAY TO SELL COMPLEX TECHNOLOGY?
COULD YOU CALL BACK? WE HAVE A BAD STRING.
1/31/01 © 2001 United Feature Syndicate, Inc.

THIS IS THE ELBONIAN FULFILLMENT SERVICE. HOW MAY I THWART YOU?
GRUNT GRUNT GRUNT GRUNT GRUNT
OKAY, IT WASN'T FUNNY THE FIRST 300 TIMES EITHER.
2/1/01 © 2001 United Feature Syndicate, Inc.

THE RESULTS OF OUR CUSTOMER SATIS-FACTION SURVEY ARE IN.
83% SPAT AT THEIR TELEPHONES UNTIL THEY DIED OF DEHYDRATION.
WE'RE CALLING THAT GROUP "THE LUCKY ONES."
2/2/01 © 2001 United Feature Syndicate, Inc.

HELLO, IS THIS THE SALES DEPARTMENT?
MAY YOU DIE A THOUSAND DEATHS BY CHOKING ON YOUR OWN BILE!
A SUPERVISOR MAY BE MONITORING THIS CALL FOR QUALITY CONTROL.
IT'S GOOD.
2/3/01 © 2001 United Feature Syndicate, Inc.

I'M A REPORTER FOR "DOGBERT'S TECHNOLOGY MAGAZINE."
I'M WRITING A TOTALLY OBJECTIVE REVIEW OF YOUR NEWEST PRODUCT.
FIRST QUESTION: WILL YOU ADVERTISE IN MY MAGAZINE OR IS YOUR NEW PRODUCT A PIECE OF JUNK?
UM...WE'LL ADVERTISE.
WILL IT BE A MULTI-PAGE AD OR IS YOUR NEW PRODUCT A PIECE OF JUNK?
©2001 United Feature Syndicate, Inc.
2/4/01
IT'LL BE A TEN-PAGE AD!
CAN YOU STAND ON YOUR HEAD FOR AN HOUR OR IS YOUR NEW PRODUCT A PIECE OF JUNK?
WOULD YOU LIKE TO SUBSCRIBE TO MY MAGAZINE? IT'S TEN PAGES OF ADS.